LIFE ON
THE EDGE

About the Author

Adrian Dangar first met Tristan Voorspuy more than thirty years ago, and with his help later established Wild & Exotic, a travel company specialising in riding safaris and tailor-made journeys around the world. He has travelled extensively throughout Africa, South America and Asia on numerous writing and travel assignments and is a regular contributor to *Country Life* and *The Field*. He has written four books since Quiller published *True to the Line*, a memoir of his career as a huntsman and Master of Foxhounds, in 2017. Adrian divides his time between rural North Yorkshire, the west coast of Scotland, and Kenya.

LIFE ON THE EDGE

Tristan Voorspuy's Fatal Love of Africa

Adrian Dangar

Quiller

Copyright © 2018, 2023 Adrian Dangar

This edition published 2023
by Quiller, an imprint of Amberley Publishing Ltd

British Library Cataloguing-in-Publication Data
A catalogue record for this book is available from
the British Library

ISBN 978 1 84689 380 3 (paperback)
ISBN 978 1 84689 267 7 (ebook)

Maps are included for illustrative purposes only and are not to scale.

Jacket designed by Guy Callaby
Internal layout by Arabella Ainslie
Front cover photograph by Adrian Dangar
Back cover photograph by Offbeat Safaris

Printed in Malta.

Quiller
An imprint of Amberley Publishing Ltd
The Hill, Merrywalks, Stroud, GL5 4EP
Tel: 01453 847800
Email: info@quillerbooks.com
Website: www.quillerpublishing.com

For those he left behind:
Cindy, Archie and Imo

Contents

Tristan Voorspuy's Kenya   viii

Foreword   xi

Introduction   xiii

1. Baptism with Fire   1
2. A Country Lad   7
3. An Officer and a Gentleman   15
4. Sussex to Cape Town   25
5. No Going Back   39
6. An African Romance   47
7. A Parting of the Ways   59
8. Building a Life in Kenya   67
9. Stories from the Sky   75
10. Of Lion and Buffalo   89
11. Life on Safari   99
12. A Nice Place to Live   111
13. Paradise Found   125
14. Of Elephants and Men   135
15. Expanding Horizons   143
16. Sosian Transformed   155
17. At the Top of His Game   163
18. Trouble in Paradise   173
19. Game Over   183
20. The Last Ride   191

Epilogue   199

Principal Characters   207

Acknowledgements   213

The Tristan Voorspuy Conservation Trust   216

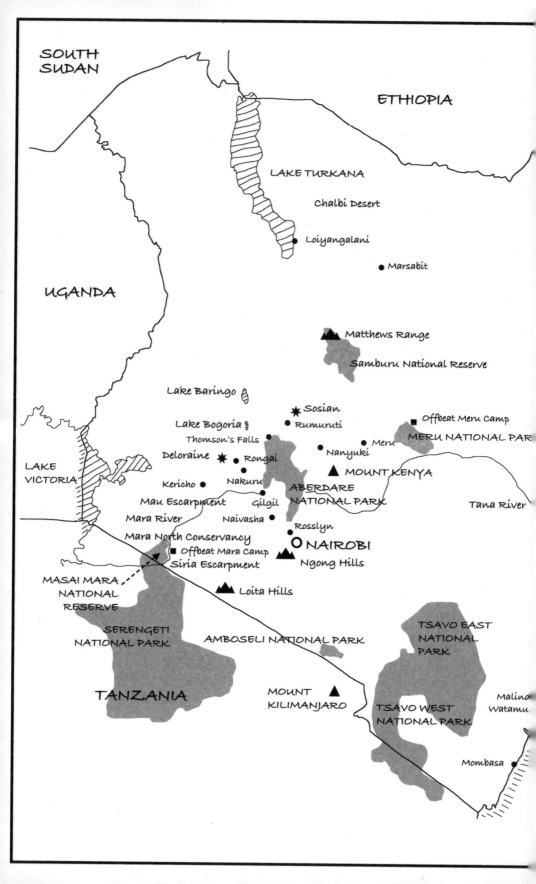

Tristan Voorspuy's Kenya

and inset Laikipia County

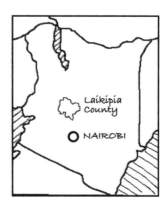

Laikipia County

◯ NAIROBI

SOMALIA

INDIAN
OCEAN

CHURO

LOUNIEK

KIRIMUN

Mugie

Laikipia
Nature Conservancy

SOSIAN

Loisaba

SAMBURU
NATIONAL
RESERVE

Kamogi

EWASO

Lorok

LAIKIPIA
NORTH

ISIOLO

Suyian

Lewa

KAMWENJE

Sosian Ranch

Ol Donyo
Lembere

Mpala

Borana

Ol Maisor

Kiwayu

Ol Jogi

RUMURUTI

THOME

Lamu

Lombala

Segera

KIFUKO

Mogwooni

LAIKIPIA
WEST

SUGUROI

Mutara

TIMAU

Ol Pejeta
Conservancy

NANYUKI

LAIKIPIA EAST

▲

MOUNT KENYA

Solio

NAIROBI

Foreword

TRISTAN Voorspuy was one of a kind. A charismatic, towering figure, he cut a swathe through society, the British Army and, above all, East Africa. Those of us lucky enough to have gone with him on his impeccably organised riding safaris will remember a superb raconteur who, after a day spent associating closely – sometimes alarmingly intimately – with a dazzling variety of wildlife, would settle down in his camp chair and, whisky in hand, round off the experience with gripping tales of his adventures. In the process, he would reveal his intimate knowledge of the birds and beasts, the environment and the people we had seen. His passion for all things African went deep and his huge efforts to establish realistic conservation to protect the landscape he loved so much and to foster good relations with the Maasai, who he admired and understood, really did make a difference.

No one is better qualified than Adrian Dangar to pay tribute to Tristan's life. Good friends for thirty years, they rode together in Argentina, Botswana, Ethiopia and Patagonia with Wild & Exotic, the company Adrian founded eighteen years ago with Tristan's help. There and, of course, in Mara, Laikipia and Amboseli, they shared the best way of travelling, where true companionship and understanding can develop properly. As a result, Tristan's serious conservation credentials are revealed alongside the fearless adventurer that many of his clients will recognise.

It is a tragedy that Tristan is no longer with us, but he will be long remembered, not least through the Foundation bearing his name. This book tells the story of a life well lived.

Robin Hanbury-Tenison

Introduction

I FIRST met Tristan Voorspuy in May 1988, when Cindy Macintosh brought her boyfriend to Cornwall, where her parents owned a cottage. I was looking after a pack of foxhounds on Dartmoor at the time, but am so glad I made arrangements to get away for the weekend and lay the foundations of a friendship that was to endure for the next thirty-odd years. Within an hour of meeting, we were striding out across wild country to relieve a remote lake on Bodmin Moor of several large trout. After that, stories kept filtering back to England of Tristan's exploits and derring-do in Africa.

Chasing a fox across the English countryside felt rather tame in comparison, and when I hung up my hunting boots, it was Tristan to whom I turned for inspiration. At his behest, I flew to Nairobi and after a late night at the Muthaiga Club, continued in his small aeroplane to join Mark Laurence, Julieta Keene and a dozen clients on a Mara riding safari. I remember the jaw-dropping expanse of the bush, the campfire camaraderie, Tristan's quiet authority and the respect he commanded. Mark was leading the ride, but Tristan was indisputably the boss.

I returned to England and founded a travel company called Wild & Exotic, and thereafter was a regular visitor to Kenya and Offbeat Safaris. Wonderfully generous, not only did Tristan introduce me to many new clients (it was meant to be the other way round), but he and Cindy were often guinea pigs on our new rides in different parts of the world. Since Offbeat has been my benchmark against which to judge all other safari operators, the Voorspuys' feedback on these exploratory rides was invaluable.

I remember Tristan being disgruntled when a flight delay resulted in us having to share a Patagonian beach with a group of singing nuns, and his delight on the same ride at seeing condors soaring in the clouds. A highly knowledgeable and infectiously enthusiastic guide on his own Kenyan safaris, Tristan was happy to take a tactful back seat in Botswana, while other guides showed us their version and vision of Africa.

As Rufus said at his brother's memorial, Tristan was one of those unusual individuals that so many people regarded as their own best friend. Few men have such a gift, and the congregation in the church at Greens Norton that July day bristled with pride. He was unflinchingly loyal to them all. While writing this book, so many of Tristan's friends and family have also remarked on his letter-writing skills and the importance he attached to staying in touch. Letters were guaranteed following any kind of hospitality, but could also be expected in times of trouble or triumph – Tristan was anything but a fair-weather friend.

A consummate all-round horseman, he was as fearless on four legs as two, and a rider who inspired similar qualities in every horse he sat on. I remember him sailing over a huge Yorkshire hedge on a novice hunter during one of his November visits to the UK, and the owner's delight that his horse had increased significantly in value. Many cherish memories of Tristan in his element in the African bush. I do, too, but the holiday we shared with Archie on the west coast of Scotland just six months before his death was memorable for the many 'Tristianisms' that took place during the week.

Having abandoned Kenya at the height of the safari season, he was determined to make the most of a boys' own holiday spent almost entirely outdoors. We walked for miles in all weathers, caught salmon, trout and mackerel, and on one unforgettable day set off to stalk a highland stag in the rain. The morning got off to an inauspicious start, when halfway up a mountain Tristan realised he had forgotten his rucksack. Had the ball been on the other foot, I reflected, I would have been facing a long walk home alone. He made amends by spotting a stag hidden amongst the boulder-strewn slopes of a precipitous mountain, and after a successful stalk insisted – almost to the point of having a scrap – on single-handedly carrying the venison home to atone for his absent rucksack. Each evening after dinner, in silence and with a whisky to hand, Tristan watched us load up the dishwasher, but the moment we finished, he carefully removed and washed every item by hand in what became a hilarious nightly ritual.

Writing Tristan's biography was never going to be easy. The greatest challenge has been to reconcile Tristan the flamboyant adventurer, who lived life permanently on the edge, with the altogether more serious

Tristan, who cared deeply about the fate of Africa and her wildlife. There have been moments during the last nine months when I have sensed his presence at my shoulder, peering at the words on my laptop, and with veins throbbing on the side of his head, aggressively jabbing the screen with his fingers. 'You can't write that,' he would fume. For me, the saddest part about this book is that the one man whose views on it I most value, is no longer here to give them.

Generous but short tempered, indulgent yet intolerant, simultaneously compassionate and fierce, Tristan was truly a man of contradictions. Such anomalies were reflected in some of his celebrated sayings. 'We are all doomed,' he would announce last thing at night, but by morning and back in the saddle, the upbeat and animated cry was often, 'Big bull elephant ahead!' I remember once, after a particularly trying day on safari, asking Tristan why he did it. He looked at me in astonishment. 'Because I dig the bush,' he said.

CHAPTER ONE

Baptism with Fire

TRISTAN Voorspuy woke two days before Christmas to the soft patter of rain on warm grass and the low rumble of African voices, as camp staff set about their work in the half light of a new dawn. He crawled from his sleeping bag, pulled on a pair of denim jeans and stood, bare-chested, to squint at the cracked mirror inside his washbag and shave with the bowl of warm water that had been left outside his tent.

The mirror reflected a face of classic good looks, high cheekbones and piercing blue eyes beneath a thick mat of tousled brown hair, but the razor cut stubble from skin flushed red by the African sun, for the twenty-eight-year-old English adventurer had landed in Nairobi only the previous week to take up the offer of a job without pay, made by a man he had never met.

With a short service commission in the British Army behind him and gripped by a childhood passion for Africa reignited during recent visits to Kenya, Tristan had written to Tony Church earlier that year asking for work with the first riding safari operator in East Africa. Tony had launched Safaris Unlimited Africa back in 1971, having invested in three horses with the sale proceeds from a set of golf clubs.

The company initially offered day rides through the Ngong Hills, overlooking the prosperous Nairobi suburb of Karen, which were immortalised in Karen Blixen's book, *Out of Africa*. As early clients discovered in a succession of hair-raising adventures, the wooded hills were still home to rhino and other big game in the seventies, but within a year Tony began to develop mobile riding safaris across the floor of the Great Rift Valley. These were supported by a team of staff, cooks and grooms travelling between campsites by vehicles, whilst the clients rode through wild country on horseback.

By the time Tristan wrote asking for work, Safaris Unlimited had established a new base at Mara River Lodge, beside the eponymous river in the Masai Mara, a wild, expansive ecosystem straddling Kenya and Tanzania, famous for vast numbers of plains game and attendant predators roaming the savannah. Huge herds of wildebeest spend their lives here in a perpetual quest for fresh grass, grazing northwards through the southern Serengeti to arrive at the Mara River from July onwards. When the lure of sweet grass on the far bank becomes too great to resist, they must run the gauntlet of hungry crocodiles and lion eager to partake in a bounteous feast. It was in this landscape of jaw-dropping beauty and dangerous wild game that Tony Church had let loose his new guide with a dozen American clients.

Having finished shaving, Tristan strode through damp grass to inspect the nineteen safari horses inside their small enclosure. As he did not yet speak or understand Swahili, the former cavalry officer could only mumble *Jambo* – the East African salutation – to the syces[1] greeting him as their new boss, but he had quiet words of comfort for each horse, as he ran his hands down front legs to check for sprains and felt behind withers for any sign of sore backs.

Tristan was nearly halfway through guiding his first riding safari, a Christmas adventure pulled together by Wyoming-based tour operators, Bayard and Mel Fox, which had begun a week earlier in the Loita Hills. With their encouragement, and the help of an experienced Kikuyu guide called Charles, campsite had been reached safely each night and the rides had been mercifully free from the sort of accidents that occasionally conspire to turn heaven into hell. Having collided with a zebra on a previous safari, Charles knew all about serious accidents first hand. The rock he fell on split his head open so deeply that the Foxes remember seeing a pulse beating through a hole in Charles's skull, but, despite his horrendous injury, the guide had remained conscious long enough to lead them safely back to camp.

No such misfortune had taken place on this safari, but the ride had been plagued by a persistent and unseasonal problem that Tristan was powerless to resolve; rain, rain and yet more unrelenting rain to lay down

---

1   A person who takes care of horses; a groom.

a green film on the land, and transform the normally dry Mara into a wet and slippery quagmire. Much to his chagrin, Tristan also discovered on the first night that some of the tents leaked profusely, and could only apologise to clients travelling on the holiday of a lifetime.

The weather may not have been ideal, but the intoxicating mix of big game, fast horses and the mesmerising beauty of the Kenyan landscape combined to ensure their contentment, in spite of the all-pervading wet. Equally important, the young English guide had already won over the American tour operators, who were impressed by riding skills honed with the Household Cavalry, his easy-going charm, and obvious love of the African bush.

On the short walk back to breakfast across squelchy ground, Tristan contemplated his great good fortune in being alive, in Africa and leading a life that would be the envy of just about every one of his many close friends. The absence of a wage and the need to forage amongst leftovers for something to eat when back at base camp – Tony Church had made it clear that he was not prepared to feed his new guide except on safaris – were minor inconveniences to endure for the excitement of life in the bush.

The weeks prior to Tristan's departure from England had been filled with regimental dinners, hunt balls, visits to London, and hunting weekends with friends in Yorkshire, Dorset and Devon, but none of them rivalled the new-found challenge in a landscape that had been tugging away at his heartstrings since early childhood in the South African veldt.

The ride left the Aitong campsite later than usual that morning; everyone was holding out for the rain to stop, and Tristan was happy to hold court over an extended breakfast beneath the mess tent's dripping awning. Several cups of coffee later, the drumming of rain on canvas suddenly ceased, to be replaced within minutes by warm, bright sunshine that set damp ground steaming like smouldering stubble fields back home.

Twenty minutes later, Tristan rode out of camp at the head of a long column of riders and headed north towards the expansive Ingilenya Plain. Raindrops glittered from thorny spikes in the sunshine, and a herd of russet-orange Thomson's gazelle lifted their elegant heads and stared motionless save for short, flickering black tails.

When Tristan spotted a dark smudge half a mile distant, he rode towards the herd of buffalo at a brisk trot, only pulling up when the animals were so close that his guests could see their wet black noses sniffing the air and discern the smooth tips of a hundred curled horns gleaming in the sunshine. Three or four lifted heads to stare straight down their noses at the strange creatures facing them, but although several riders threw nervous glances in the direction of their guide, the tourists stood their ground.

The herd were feasting on green grass enriched by days of heavy rain, their muddy backs glistening different shades of grey in deference to the drying sun. Before leaving the buffalo to enjoy the pasture in peace, Tristan explained how the drab oxpeckers flitting between them sometimes betrayed the presence of dangerous bachelor bulls hidden in thick scrub. Then he squeezed his horse's ribs and grinned mischievously. 'Time for a gallop,' he said. 'Let's find some elephant before lunch.'

It was late afternoon by the time Tristan led the group into a campsite that had been carefully dismantled after breakfast, transported by Land Cruiser and re-sited ten miles to the west on a bend of the brown Mara River. The Siria Escarpment rose steeply from the plains beyond the water, her thorny face a darker shade of green than the lush savannah below. Menacing black clouds massed on the horizon above the ridge, banishing the sun and promising more wet weather to come. Weary riders removed saddles and bridles from their horses, before turning them out into a makeshift paddock enclosed by battery-powered electric fencing.

After that it was time to find tents, pull off sweaty boots and wash away the grime of a long ride beneath one of the hot bush showers prepared by camp staff. The guests could hear hippos grunting contentedly from a pool below the mess tent, and were looking forward to a closer look on the walk Tristan had promised before sunset.

The tranquil setting was suddenly shattered by an anguished shout, which brought Tristan running from the mess tent just in time to see the last of his nineteen horses galloping flat out into the bush. There was no time for recriminations – it later transpired the last one to be turned out had spooked the others into charging the flimsy electric fence – only for action.

Grabbing some tack, Tristan ran to the Land Cruiser, yelled for Mel and Charles to jump in beside him, and set off behind horses galloping back to where they had spent the previous night. When it became clear the runaways had no intention of stopping, their pursuers gave up the futile chase and instead drove straight to the campsite at Aitong.

They arrived in fading light to find most of the horses milling about, some grazing quietly with lowered heads, others still jumpy and fired up by their ten-mile race through the bush. Tristan walked up to a bay gelding called King Kong, and with a few tender words slipped the bridle reins over his neck. After Mel had tacked up Shaba and fastened head collars on two more, they were ready to retrace their steps back to the Mara River on a journey that had taken five hours to complete earlier the same day.

Leaving Charles to return by vehicle, Tristan gathered up King Kong's reins and encouraged the gelding into a low, loping canter across the darkening sward, as Mel chivvied the others to keep the leader in sight. Tristan made no effort to avoid aardvark holes lurking like traps to snap a horse's leg in two, but relied on King Kong's instinct and experience to cross the broken ground safely, as they cantered on towards brooding black storm clouds resting on top of the escarpment.

The sun drops like a stone on the equator, and by the time Tristan and Mel had crossed the open plains, darkness had swamped the Mara on a night so black that neither person would ever experience its equal in the years ahead. In these conditions, a heightened sense of hearing amplifies every rustle, noise and cracking branch to an alarming degree, but the riders let their horses have their heads, trusting sure-footedness and accuracy on the long journey home.

As they rode in single file through the scrub, an orchestra of strange noises filled the night air; the distant, guttural roar of lion mingling with the hollow whoop of skulking hyena, and the constant crashing of undergrowth as unidentified animals fled the troop of advancing horses. Tristan had no idea how many were left, but he had heard at least two sets of strumming hoof beats disappearing into the night.

As the river at last drew near, thickets of whistling thorn were so dense in places that the horses refused to move forward and were forced to back out of the scrub, with hooked thorns tearing at the flesh of both horse and rider. When the horses planted hooves firmly into the ground and snorted through flared nostrils at some unidentified danger, nothing would persuade them to budge, and there was no option but to retreat and circumnavigate the trouble. Finally, and after what felt like an eternity, Tristan heard the welcome rumble of the Mara River and the thorn country was at last behind them.

Relief at having reached the last stage of the journey evaporated when an enormous hippo crossed the path ten yards ahead, in a whirlwind of shaking bushes, and crashed violently into the river. Tristan knew how fast hippos can move on dry land, and that more people are killed by the semi-aquatic mammal than any other wild animal in Africa; he also knew they like to graze a long way from water at night, and if disturbed, will trample anyone in the way as they charge back to the safety of the river.

Tristan and Mel were held up several times by hippo crossing the path in front of them before they spotted the twinkling kerosene lamps of camp. Seven horses had made it safely home through the night, but there were another dozen unaccounted for in a hostile landscape teeming with predators.

Several whiskies later, and with the rain once more beating down on his tent, Tristan opened the slender, leather-bound Smythson Badminton Sporting Diary he had brought out from England and wrote in blue biro under Friday, 23rd December 1983: 'Mel and I ride missing horses home on a hairy ride reaching camp at 9.30 p.m.' He spent Christmas Eve and Christmas Day searching for them with Charles in pouring rain, but was not able to record all safely home until Boxing Day. 'Thank God,' he wrote of the last horse's return to camp that afternoon, and his first big test as a safari guide safely overcome.

+ CHAPTER TWO +

A Country Lad

TRISTAN'S nocturnal adventure through the African bush might not have ended so happily without the benefit of a carefree, rural childhood, which spanned two continents and revolved around the great outdoors, nature and wildlife. Born into a Dutch farming family in 1919, Tristan's father, Hendrik (Henk) Voorspuy, was based with an officer flying-training unit near Rotterdam, when the Germans invaded Holland in 1940.

His unit initially escaped to Caen in France, and then spent four months in England, before completing their training in Surabaya in the Dutch East Indies colony of East Java. The boat voyage there from Europe was broken by a short stay in the South African town of Durban, which was Henk's first introduction to the African country that was later to become his home.

The Japanese invasion of the Pacific in 1941 forced another move, this time to England, where Flight Officer Henk Voorspuy joined a Royal Dutch Naval Air squadron flying patrols and anti-shipping attacks above the North Sea from bases in Lancashire and Norfolk. His squadron was reassigned to Bomber Command in 1943, and equipped with American-designed B25 Mitchell bombers, to target strategic sites within France and Germany for the remainder of the Second World War.

By 1944, Flight Lieutenant Henk Voorspuy was flying bombing sorties from Dunsfold in Surrey, but in March that year his plane was hit by enemy flak when returning from a raid above France prior to the Normandy landings. The B25 bomber came down in the English Channel, but captain and crew were all safely rescued after a Walrus amphibious aircraft responded to their mayday call. The Walrus's pilot, Flight Lieutenant Wally Wallens, was astonished to recognise Henk, who had occupied the hospital bed next door to his earlier in the war.

Henk's troubles were not quite over, for when celebrating that evening wearing a borrowed RAF uniform, the Dutchman was arrested by military police on suspicion of being a spy, and only released after Wally intervened to save him for the second time in twenty-four hours. By the end of the war, Henk had flown more than eighty missions with Bomber Command, and was one of forty-four Dutch airmen to be awarded the Distinguished Flying Cross by Queen Wilhelmina of the Netherlands.

Shortly after his rescue from the English Channel, Henk met Pearl Glessing, who was working as a land girl on her parents' farm at Bexhill on the Sussex south coast. The couple were married there in March 1947, by which time Henk was working as a pilot for the Dutch airline, KLM, based at Schiphol in Amsterdam. The following year, the Voorspuys moved to South Africa after Henk accepted a KLM posting to Johannesburg.

The young couple set up home in a small village called Henley on Klip, beside a tributary of the mighty Vaal River between Johannesburg and Vereeniging, where there were no tarmac roads, no electricity and only a wind-up, party-line telephone with which to contact the outside world. Whenever possible, the Voorspuys travelled extensively from this base, including an expedition to the Rwenzori Mountains in Uganda, during an era when travel anywhere in Africa was compromised by a lack of even the most basic infrastructure.

Pearl bore her husband three children in Rufus, Morven, and Sorrel during the first five years of marriage, and conceived a fourth, unplanned sibling during a romantic break to Mauritius. Born in Johannesburg on 26th March 1955, Tristan Maarten Voorspuy spent the first three years of an idyllic early childhood roaming barefoot and shirtless on the surrounding veldt.

The Klip River flowed through the bottom of the family garden, which Rufus and Morven were allowed to swim across to play on a trapeze the other side. When this privilege was denied to their three-year-old brother, he pushed his sister into the river in an outburst of frustrated rage. For a few anxious seconds Sorrel disappeared completely from sight, but was rescued from a watery grave by a quick-thinking grown-up.

Tristan was already fascinated by the South African wildlife surrounding his home, when the family returned to Sussex in 1958 and purchased Folkington Place, a beautiful period house set in fourteen acres of grounds at the foot of the South Downs, complete with paddocks, garden and an old-fashioned farmyard.

Pearl at once set about transforming Folkington into a warm family home, and entertaining in her own inimitable style, often alone, for her husband was frequently away on flying duties. It has been said that anybody and everybody loved Pearl, a fact that was to be recorded for posterity by the inscription, 'Adored and loved by all', on her gravestone in Folkington church many years later.

Soon after the family's arrival, a middle-aged spinster named Miss Coventry offered her services as a gardener at Folkington, where she had worked for a previous owner. Pearl was rewarded for taking her on with fresh-cut flowers from the garden every day for the next thirty-five years. Miss Coventry – never Priscilla – took up residence in a small cottage by the old Tudor barn and presided over an expansive walled garden that was the envy of the locality.

The gardener became a close family friend and grew so fond of the Voorspuys' youngest son that she happily tended his marijuana plants whenever Tristan was absent during his teenage years, and left him enough money when she died to pay for his first light aircraft. He was adored by his mother, too, and although Pearl would never admit to having a favourite child, there is little doubt that Tristan was the apple of her eye.

A keen naturalist and botanist herself, Pearl derived enormous pleasure from Tristan's increasing awareness of the nature and natural history surrounding their Sussex home, and secretly admired the growing collection of stuffed birds and animals crammed into his bedroom, alongside pet hamsters, slowworms, sticklebacks, stone loaches and an exotic praying mantis. A pair of salamanders ordered by Sorrel from Harrods as a twelfth birthday present for her brother arrived through the post three weeks later, but were kept in the greenhouse rather than in Tristan's bedroom.

There were newts with fiery red bellies and dragon-like crests to be captured from the cellar at his grandparent's farm at Howard's Lodge near Bexhill, and on one memorable occasion a fat green adder with a thick black, zigzag stripe along his back. Tristan picked up the poisonous snake by the tail, and carried it in triumph out onto the lawn, where the adder was allowed to slither off to safety. He deplored the gratuitous killing of snakes from that day on, but never lost his fascination for catching, handling and releasing reptiles, especially huge pythons in the African bush.

More conventional family pets included a feisty Jack Russell terrier called Voetsek – the word means 'bugger off' in Afrikaans – that accompanied Tristan on his rambles through the Sussex countryside and frequently disappeared off rabbiting for days on end.

Although never entirely comfortable with the killing of any animal, Pearl appreciated hunting's long-standing and important role in the rural community and made sure there were ponies for her children to ride and hunt with the local East Sussex and Romney Marsh hounds. However, their first journeys on horseback were five-mile rides during school holidays between Folkington and Hankham, where the Glessing cousins farmed at Montague.

Tristan's first school was also at Hankham, although the young boy with long blond curls and flip flops was teased mercilessly by the village children, who goaded him with the words 'girlie, girlie' at every opportunity – but there were loyal friends nearby, too, many of them destined to last a lifetime. These included Freddie Menzies, whose mother, Kay Stammers, won the Wimbledon women's doubles title twice in the 1930s and had become a close friend of Pearl's when the two families lived only an hour's drive apart in South Africa.

A quartet of semi-feral children roaming the Sussex countryside was completed by Martyn Lee, who also lived locally, and the Voorspuys' younger cousin, Sophia Glessing. Sophia was allowed to tag along and carry whatever vermin the boys managed to shoot with a .177 air rifle; she was rather taken for granted, and in an oblique reference to African big game hunters, was referred to somewhat high-handedly as 'the bearer' during lengthy incursions onto other people's property.

In the absence of anything better or more exciting to aim at, the boys occasionally resorted to firing at each other, which resulted in Freddie shooting out one of Tristan's teeth instead of aiming for his legs as agreed. Knowing that Pearl would be furious, the boys hatched an elaborate plan that resulted in a toothless Tristan returning home following a lengthy detour, to explain to his bemused mother that he had broken the tooth tripping over barbed wire. The ruse fooled no one, but Tristan's willingness to cover up his friend's crime did not go unnoticed.

As a pilot working for KLM, Henk was able to fly his family around the world at reduced cost, which meant that school holidays often included visits to faraway exotic destinations such as Argentina, where the Voorspuys spent four different Christmases staying with friends at Estancia La Colina in San Luis Province. The children loved their time at the old-fashioned estancia, where the nearest house was five miles away and the family home was powered by a diesel Lister generator. Tristan found its comforting thump particularly alluring and decided that he would one day live in a house where electricity was provided the same way.

In time the village school was exchanged for a proper haircut and prep school in Eastbourne, which led in turn to O and A Levels at Eastbourne College. Pearl was too fond of her children to allow them to board, explaining to anyone who questioned her decision that she wanted to watch them grow up herself. Instead they caught the school bus every morning when it stopped at the end of the mile-long lane connecting Folkington Place with the A27, leaving their bikes at the housekeeper's cottage nearby.

As the children grew older, they began to spend more time during spring and summer holidays at an enchanting mill house perched on the banks of the River Taw, beneath Exmoor's wild moorland in Devon. Pearl's father had spotted the derelict, tin-roofed house through the treetops when filling his car up with petrol in 1942, and purchased the property for the princely sum of £100. It took the Voorspuys eight hours to travel there from Folkington in Henk's Borgward Station Waggon crammed full of children, provisions and equipment.

The Mill was a wilder home from home, where the children and their Glessing cousins enjoyed carefree, day-long excursions deep into the Devon countryside and sunny afternoons immersed in the River Taw, which furnished them with eels to smoke in the fireplace chimney and the occasional silver salmon landed by fair means or foul. The children never knew what to expect on these adventures and were struck with wonder when a large mink swam between their legs during a fishing expedition for stone loach. At sunset they returned to a roaring log fire, fed by driftwood collected from the mill race, and ate at a vast refectory table hewn from an enormous elm planted to commemorate the restoration of Charles II on their great uncle's Compton Chamberlayne estate.

Tristan first read and absorbed *Tarka the Otter* and *Salar the Salmon* at the same wooden table, drawing inspiration from Henry Williamson's detailed observations on nature, wildlife, and the unspoilt North Devon countryside defined by the rivers Torridge and Taw. The books made a lasting impression and were held up by Tristan as the finest natural history prose ever written.

There was room for twenty around the huge table, which was perfect for teenage parties and the long, wild weekends that were later to become a feature of Tristan's infrequent visits to England. As a second lieutenant in the Blues and Royals, he was astonished to meet a soldier some years later in Germany who knew all about the wild weekend parties and topless sunbathing that went on at The Mill. 'It just goes to show how much of what we get up to down there is noticed,' Tristan observed in a letter to Sorrel, 'and it made me realise that nothing is secret.'

Wild parties were becoming increasingly frequent by the time Tristan left Eastbourne College, and as irrepressibly high spirits took hold of the Voorspuy siblings, local pubs such as The Yew Tree at Chalvington and The Sussex Ox in Milton Street became familiar rowdy haunts. Pearl got used to answering the doorbell to uniformed police officers with the salutation, 'Good morning, officer, which one of them would you like to see today?', although Tristan escaped arrest having downed several pints of cider and streaking naked across the Broad Oak point-to-point course at Heathfield in 1974. The *Sussex Express* reporter writing up the day's racing ended his piece by noting that a streaker went to ground in the woods at the northern edge of the course.

An altercation with hunt saboteurs resulted in a court appearance later the same year when Tristan and a family friend, Robin Knight Bruce, were defended by a solicitor who happened to be a local master of hounds. The students took great exception at being charged £50 for the services of a fellow country sportsman, but gained their revenge when the hapless man walked into The Plough at Udimore a week later, where he was strung up on a coat hook by Rufus Voorspuy, and relieved of the cash he had earned as a result of their misfortunes.

Departure from Eastbourne College was celebrated by a road trip with school friends through France that ended up at a camp site in Monaco, where the tents were pitched on a series of narrow terraces. One of his companions remembers Tristan emerging naked from his tent after a heavy night, only to trip over a guy rope and crash belly down onto a table of Germans enjoying their breakfast ten feet below. Having swept the detritus of bacon and eggs from his naked backside, the young man slid off the table, stood up straight and mumbled, 'I'm terribly sorry about that,' before heading off to the loo.

On his return to England, Tristan moved into a cottage near Rye with the Menzies brothers to begin the year's practical farming that was a condition of entry into the Royal Agricultural College (RAC) at Cirencester. His duties working for Frank Reeve at Peasmarsh included grooming the MFH's horses and taking them hunting with the East Sussex and Romney Marsh hounds.

In between farming, hunting and pub crawls, Tristan met and fell in love with his landlord's daughter, Claire Mair, but when his first serious relationship ended several months later, the young farm student was heartbroken. Morven came to the rescue by whisking his younger brother off to Kenya on his first ever visit to the country that he was destined to one day call home.

In March 1974, the brothers landed in Nairobi and drove north via Thomson's Falls to the gateway of Kenya's northern Laikipia District at Rumuruti, to stay with the Voorspuys' former South African neighbours, Tom and Winkie Bower, for whom Morven had worked during his own gap year four years earlier. Tom now managed the beautiful Mutara Ranch, a landscape of undulating grass plains dotted with acacia thorn trees and herds of wild game roaming either side of the Ewaso Nyiro River. The Bowers entertained their guests on the ranch, and introduced them to the Rumuruti Club, where families and neighbours gathered twice weekly to play tennis and billiards, drink beer and meet friends.

They were joined at Mutara by some of Tom's Nairobi friends for a boy's own Land Rover safari to the remote, lunar landscape surrounding the emerald green waters of Lake Rudolf. The friends took along a small complement of Mutara staff to look after them, and were greeted on arrival at the isolated outpost of Loiyangalani by members of the nomadic Rendille tribe, whose ancestors from Southern Ethiopia settled the area following centuries of conflict over grazing and water with the rival Oromo tribe.

The next day a Rendille tribesman paddled Tom and Tristan through the lake's crocodile-infested waters to catch Nile perch that tasted delicious when cooked over an open fire. The safari continued across the barren Chalbi Desert, where Tristan overcame his lost Sussex love and began to fall for Kenya instead.

Tents were exchanged for the facilities of a semi-permanent camp at Marsabit, where the famous elephant Ahmed[2] had recently been discovered dead of old age by the armed guards appointed to protect him. As if to compensate, an elephant sauntered through the middle of camp at dusk whilst the group were enjoying a cold beer; Tristan watched his slow progress in awe, mesmerised by the soft, gentle footsteps, thick ivory tusks and long lashes draped over small black eyes, blinking from folds of crinkled grey skin.

After the safari ended, the brothers extended their stay with a visit to the Indian Ocean at Malindi, travelling there by matatu[3] in some discomfort. They returned after a relaxing stay at the Driftwood Hotel sandwiched between two air hostesses from British Airways, which Tristan pointed out, was an altogether better experience than the journey down.

---

2   Ahmed was reputed to have roamed Marsabit National Park in the North of Kenya for over fifty years. It was claimed that his tusks were so large that he could rest his head on them. In 1970, he was protected by presidential decree and lived the rest of his life looked after by armed guards. When he died of natural causes in 1974, it was estimated from the weight of his tusks that he was sixty-five years old.

3   Privately owned minibus operating as a shared taxi.

* CHAPTER THREE *

An Officer and a Gentleman

BACK home with his spirits restored, Tristan went to Cirencester in the autumn of 1975, but over exuberance, a predilection for whisky, and a healthy disregard for authority all came together after a night of drinking and dancing at the Queen Charlotte's Ball for debutantes in London. Mr Greenwood is known to generations of RAC students as the stern-faced lecturer on land law, and a man who does not suffer fools gladly.

The truculent student at the back of the classroom had already interrupted his lecture twice, when a three-quarter's empty bottle of scotch rolled purposefully down the aisle to come to rest at his feet. That was quite enough for Mr Greenwood, who muttered something dark about Tristan in particular and the Voorspuy brothers in general, gathered up his books and stormed out of the lecture hall.

Henk's disappointment at his son's dismissal from college, following a long run of bad behaviour abated somewhat after Tristan responded to an advertisement for army officers in the *Daily Telegraph* and had his application for Sandhurst accepted following two days of appraisal by the Regular Commissions Board at Westbury. New recruits are confined to barracks for the first month at Sandhurst, but Tristan won the admiration of his colleagues by escaping during the first week to attend a friend's twenty-first birthday in Kent. The bleary-eyed officer cadet, who showed up at the main Sandhurst gates dressed in civilian clothes at 5.30 a.m., had to charm his way back in past his colleague, Pip Astley Birtwistle, on guard duty.

'You're Pip, aren't you,' smiled Tristan, reading the name printed on the guard's lapel. 'I believe we have a mutual friend in Martyn Lee, I've just seen him at a party. We really must all get together for a drink.'

Only twenty minutes' drive from Sandhurst, well-bred young ladies were taught cookery, dressmaking, flower arranging and other domestic skills inside an imposing white country house surrounded by sprawling gardens on the edge of Windsor Forest. Winkfield Place was close enough for regular dances with the trainee officers at Sandhurst, where Tristan homed in on a slim blonde student called Katie Girardet. The young lovers met whenever the strict regime of Sandhurst permitted, but drifted apart after his regiment was posted to Germany — but not before Kate had introduced the officer cadet to her friend and colleague, Elizabeth Ryrie.

The nineteen-year-old was poised, attractive, intelligent and fun, but Tristan was equally smitten by the fact that his new friend had been brought up at a beautiful colonial house in Kenya, where her mother still lived. As it turned out, he did not have to wait long before visiting Rosslyn, but any dreams of a return to Africa were postponed whilst he knuckled down to work at Sandhurst, and he was rewarded by promotion to the rank of cadet corporal.

Days before his passing-out parade, six months of Sandhurst were almost wasted when a small group of friends decided on having a party, which kicked off with Pimm's beside the lake in front of the old college and ended up at Barossa Common, where the men had spent several nights on training exercise. Pip Astley Birtwistle, a firm friend ever since his dawn encounter with Tristan at the start of the course, was designated to drive a group of officer cadets back to barracks, which included the future British Army spokesman in Bosnia, Chris Vernon (later elevated to hero status by his peers on account of his seduction techniques and successes) and Robin Knight Bruce. Everything was going according to plan, until Pip swerved violently to avoid running over a dog, and the car and its drunken occupants ended upside down in a ditch.

The reprobates were rounded up and frogmarched into the officers' mess for a dressing down by the duty officer, which Tristan found shoulder-shakingly hilarious. When asked by his superior exactly what he found so very funny, Tristan could offer no explanation other than a prolonged fit of uncontrollable giggles, so his friend came to the rescue.

'This time next week, he's going to be an officer in the Blues and Royals,' said Pip, looking down his nose at his superior. 'In fact, we'll both be cavalry officers by then, and won't be speaking to oiks like you anymore.' The pair were thrown into cells for a few hours to cool off and summoned to appear in front of the college commander, Colonel Smyth-Osbourne, early the following morning.

By dawn the enormity of their predicament had become painfully clear to both miscreants, who feared the prospect of a sudden and shameful end to their military careers. They narrowly escaped this disgrace, but Cadet Corporal Voorspuy walked out of the colonel's office having been demoted to plain officer cadet and lost the stripe he had worked so hard to achieve. This healthy cynicism towards authority never left Tristan, and was to characterise his progress through life.

A few days later, Henk and Pearl were proud spectators when their youngest son passed out of Sandhurst as a second lieutenant, or cornet, as newly commissioned officers are referred to in the Blues and Royals. Tristan had been persuaded to apply for the distinguished Household Cavalry regiment following a chance meeting with their hunting officer[4] the previous year, and his service with them was to garner friendships that lasted for life.

Most of the young officers passing out of Sandhurst had never seen a tank close up, yet alone driven or fired one, but during the next few weeks they assimilated both skills at a troop leader's course in Dorset for young officers from several different regiments. The driver and maintenance course at Bovington was followed by a gunnery course at Lulworth, where the subalterns learnt how to handle tanks and armoured cars.

With the boarding school atmosphere of Sandhurst now a distant memory, high-spirited young officers were suddenly at liberty to spend their time off duty as they pleased. Dorset was much further from London than Surrey, but parties in the capital were marked by a fleet of old bangers heading east up the motorway at dusk, driven by immaculate young men wearing dinner jackets and bow ties.

---

4   An officer from the Household Cavalry in charge of army-owned black horses, based at Melton Mowbray for hunting and training with Leicestershire hunts.

The Blues and Royals' posting to Detmold in Germany that autumn was a culture shock to subalterns used to racing up to London at the drop of a hat, although Tristan quickly found entertainment with the army's Weser Vale pack of bloodhounds, and there would be regimental polo tournaments to look forward to in the summer, after return from a tour of duty in Northern Ireland.

Tristan wrote frequently to his sister from Germany, describing training exercises for his imminent posting as arduous and begging her to organise some entertainment for his leave between tours. With characteristic enterprise, he also wrote to the British Army in Kenya, explaining that he was an officer in the Blues and Royals, and asking for permission to rent their Land Rovers and equipment for a safari the following year.

The monotonous reality of life as an officer in Northern Ireland became apparent soon after Tristan's arrival in Londonderry in January 1977 as a troop leader in charge of sixteen men, split into four units for the purpose of street patrols and surveillance, in a city of discontent torn between republican Roman Catholics and loyalist British Protestants.

Although Cornet Voorspuy quickly earned the respect of the men in his troop, it became clear that there were going to be few, if any, opportunities to put skills learnt in Germany to good use in combat.

'I rather wish something would happen,' Tristan complained to his sister when congratulating Sorrel on her engagement, 'because at the moment the whole place seems completely dead. We never get out unless we are armed to the teeth, but can see the lovely Donegal Mountains so close, yet so far, and yet never get the time or a vehicle to go there, which is very frustrating.'

He also commented on the ugly slums and housing estates where the residents used their gardens as giant dustbins. Some of the occupants were described as amiable, others were plain bloody minded, but the worst were terrorists known to be responsible for all kinds of atrocities. 'It just goes to show that you can trust nobody,' he concluded, before signing off at 2.00 a.m. by apologising for a lethargic letter with the words, 'but that is how one feels after 6 hours in a chair with nothing happening.'

Unlike Sandhurst, Bovington or even Germany, attractive girls to alleviate the boredom were few and far between. 'All the pretty girls are in London and none of them stay here between one Christmas and the next. Life is extremely dull and everyone is really beginning to loathe it,' he lamented in another letter to Sorrel.

With his first tour of Northern Ireland complete, it was back to Germany before a return to Pirbright in Surrey, where Tristan learnt that his request for army Land Rovers in Kenya had been favourably received. With four weeks' leave successfully negotiated during late September and early October, Tristan and Morven flew out to Nairobi, where they were joined by a group that included Elizabeth Ryrie, Chris Vernon from Sandhurst, and his childhood friends, the Menzies brothers, Freddie and Mark.

The friends headed north to Samburu Land in two Land Rovers with Sonia Ryrie's cook to look after them, and they returned via Lake Baringo on the floor of the Rift Valley, where they saw hippo and giant Nile crocodiles. They wound down at the coast after a visit to the spectacular Masai Mara National Reserve and three separate stays at Rosslyn, where they enjoyed Sonia Ryrie's generous hospitality and early morning rides on her horses.

Elizabeth's family had come to live at Rosslyn in 1963, and Sonia was to remain in residence at the Nairobi house, where Tristan could expect a warm welcome for the rest of his life. The charming, single-storey building had been built by a white hunter called Major Andy Anderson in 1919 and was known for the copperplate inscription on the dining room ceiling indicating the 12 feet 2 inches height of a record elephant he had shot, which had been much admired by Edward, Prince of Wales, when he dined there.

Andy was nicknamed Mguu – meaning leg in Swahili – by his gun bearer, after severe mauling by a lion left him with a permanent limp, and he was a founder member of the East Africa Professional Hunters Association. Many years later, the house was back in the limelight as a location for the 2005 film, *The Constant Gardener*.

In common with the Prince of Wales and the film's producers, Tristan was charmed by the intimate, sun-drenched courtyard packed with rampant foliage, bright potted flowers and a leafy Mulberry tree to shade the stone-flagged floor. A wrap-around veranda led to a large drawing room filled with light and fresh flowers, where evocative black-and-white family photographs jostled for space on a stone mantelpiece above the fireplace.

Lionel Edwards' hunting prints reminded Sonia of a rural English upbringing, and a heavy wooden chest dating from the Battle of Waterloo occupied a corner of the dining room. Manicured lawns sloped gently away from stone terraces, where Tristan sat down to admire exotic entries such as fantail snipe, bronze-capped teal and blue-breasted quail, meticulously recorded in a family game book.

The outlook is very different now, but at the time of his first visit in 1977, the views beyond lawns shaded by purple blossomed jacaranda trees were to rolling countryside and shimmering green coffee plantations. When the others flew back to England, the Voorspuy brothers visited a second expat spinster in Ann Joyce, who farmed at Kilima Kiu – meaning thirsty hill in Swahili – overlooking the Athi River. The brothers were amused to see her staff running from one place to the next as they went about their tasks, following the example of the head butler called Mui, who was known throughout colonial Kenya as 'The Galloping Butler'.

Tristan's return to Kenya had been a fabulous success and the highlight of an otherwise frustrating year, only tarnished for the young officer by the fact that Elizabeth Ryrie was on Mark Menzies' arm for the duration of the safari, and not his.

Elizabeth was ultimately unable to resist the twinkle in her admirer's eye, his old-fashioned courtesies and infectious giggles, and the two friends were very much a couple by the time they returned to Kenya for another safari two years later, where the camping gear and Land Rovers were again supplied by the Kahawa Army Barracks on the outskirts of Nairobi.

That trip is remembered for Tristan's argument in Samburu National Park with a Frenchman who had joined the party. When he could no longer bear the frustrations of a futile, late-night debate, Tristan suddenly stood up from his chair, shouted, 'Stuff this!', and marched military style straight into the crocodile-infested waters of the Ewaso Ng'iro River. The others looked on in astonishment as the Ryries' cook assisted the enraged Englishman out of the water. Having made his point and cooled off, a soaking wet Tristan poured himself another large whisky and returned to his seat by the fire as if nothing had happened.

Tristan's behaviour that night may have been the culmination of months of pent-up angst and frustration with his military circumstances, compounded by a bad return tour to Northern Ireland for his regiment earlier the same year. He was despairing of life in the army, when he wrote to his sister from a rain-swept Germany in September 1978, several months before his tour of West Belfast, complaining bitterly that he had been home for only one weekend since April. He described an exciting hunt with the bloodhounds, but the onset of a new hunting season only made him homesick for life back home.

He admitted to 'unbearable depressions when I think of what I miss in England while being out here,' and lamented the constant moving between Germany, England and Northern Ireland that is the hallmark of a serving officer's life.

'I really wonder what the hell I am getting out of it,' he scrawled, 'these last six weeks have made me so bitter and twisted towards the army that it is quite unbelievable.' He was dreading a return to Northern Ireland the following spring, and another year of youth lost through 'being out of touch with everything I enjoy.' Tristan rarely shared such dark thoughts with those around him and concealed his frustrations by enthusing about sport with the bloodhounds and a forthcoming regimental skiing trip to St Moritz.

The 1979 West Belfast tour started well when Tristan found himself sharing a room with Martin Horsford, who has been described as an archetypal cavalry officer with a sharp wit and a sense of fun. Martin wasted no time in redecorating their shabby accommodation, forcing his room-mate to pick up a paintbrush until their sleeping quarters were the envy of his squadron's officers, and a reassuring man-cave retreat.

However, the tour was to be plunged into disarray by an infamous Blues and Royals incident that resulted in two men dead from friendly fire. Tristan was relaxing in the officers' mess with Martin on the evening of 25th February 1979, as a soldiers' party got underway in the assembly hall nearby, despite the troop leaders having expressed reservations to their senior officer about alcohol being served to men on duty.

Their worst fears were confirmed when shots suddenly rang out from the darkness, followed by a corporal of horse[5] rushing into the officers' mess instructing everyone to get down and lie still. Tristan and his friends were itching to get outside into the night and help with whatever was going on, but the awful reality became clear soon enough. Fuelled by drink, and teetering on the edge of sanity following weeks of dangerous patrols, a young trooper[6] on his way to sangar guard duty[7] had opened fire and hit two of his own colleagues before being shot in turn to prevent further carnage.

The end of that tour could not come soon enough, and a posting to join the Household Cavalry Mounted Regiment at Knightsbridge saw Tristan's spirits soar, as he was once more surrounded by friends in the familiar city of London. Having persuaded Elizabeth Ryrie into a romantic relationship, he was now stationed close to his new girlfriend's flat in Queen's Gate. With the best parties only a short drive away in his pale blue Deux Chevaux, it was as if Northern Ireland were only a bad dream, although the horrific exploits of the IRA were permanently in the news, to remind Tristan of his good fortune in arriving safely home.

Under these circumstances, it was hardly surprising that policemen warmed to young men with short back and sides and good manners to match, and subalterns a little the worse for wear were frequently advised to park up or hand over the keys to their cars when driving home from parties. They were rarely arrested or charged, although Tristan was lucky to escape with a caution after a police car chase down the Cromwell Road ended abruptly down a dead end amongst a heap of dustbins.

'I'm absolutely done for now,' he told Elizabeth as he staggered out of the car to face the music and direct every ounce of his boyish charm at the policeman confronting him. 'Awful thing is, I think I'm being posted back to Northern Ireland next week,' he mumbled contritely as a necessary white lie. The policeman decided against the breathalyser, but instructed

---

5 An equivalent rank to sergeant in other regiments.

6 An equivalent rank to private in other regiments.

7 A sangar is a protected sentry post, normally located around the perimeter of a base. Its main function is to provide early warning of attack to protect forces both within the base and those deployed within sight of the sangar.

the polite young man to take his missus home in a taxi, and not, under any circumstances, drive his car again that night.

The Knightsbridge posting also offered Tristan the opportunity to resume his career as an amateur jockey and enjoy sport in High Leicestershire riding the army's black horses at Melton Mowbray. He had harboured ambitions to win a race since his point-to-point debut in Sussex a few years earlier, and infrequent appearances on the racecourse were supported by loyal friends, who applauded their hero's disarming readiness to laugh off his failures. He rode Tangled Knight, trained by his brother Rufus, in the prestigious 1981 Grand Military Steeplechase at Sandown and pulled up two fences from home, but was delighted to have outstayed the Prince of Wales, who had fallen off earlier in the race.

That performance was considerably better than a previous and ungainly tumble on the flat at a local point-to-point, a mishap that infuriated Rufus, who attributed Tristan's fall to excessive fortification prior to the race. Tristan never rode into the winner's enclosure, but he did have his way with his brother's head girl in the hay barn at Folkington. 'I wondered why my horses wouldn't eat their hay,' was all Rufus said after the event.

With his short service commission coming to an end, and disappointed by uneventful tours of duty with the Blues and Royals, in 1981 Tristan set his sights on joining the SAS, a special forces unit of the British Army whose covert reconnaissance, counter-terrorism and hostage-rescue activities are shrouded in secrecy. He knew that acceptance would guarantee action around the world, but not until he had completed an arduous selection process that included a brutal endurance test in the Brecon Beacons. Many candidates had already dropped out by this stage of the course, but Tristan was amongst a dozen officer recruits still standing in August 1981, when he was dropped off in a rainstorm at the base of Pen y Fan for a solitary forty-mile march up, down and around the mountain.

Tristan felt confident, fit and strong; he had already impressed selectors by joining them for a drink one evening whilst his companions had lain exhausted in bed, and only needed to complete the march before moving on to Officer's Week and the final stage of selection. He reached each checkpoint in time, despite strong winds, intermittent rain and a 55lb rucksack on his back, but shortly after dawn decided to take a direct route through the vast forestry plantation that stood between him and the next rendezvous. He went into the woodland ahead of schedule and full of running but was soon battling through dense timber after his short cut led into a sprawling plantation of near impenetrable young trees.

Two voices were at work inside his head as Tristan stumbled onwards in a battle with the branches. The voice of reason urged him to retreat and circumnavigate the trouble, but the stronger voice prevailed, and he lurched determinedly onwards through the cloying gloom. By the time he reached the next checkpoint, every muscle in his body ached, and his knees felt like they were on fire. 'Fuck it,' he said to the instructor as he sank down into the comforting grass. 'That's it. I've had enough.'

Ten minutes later, his colleague Peter Bateman arrived, having taken the longer but easier route, and implored him to complete the final ninety minutes. Tristan watched his friend continue, clambered back to his feet and told the instructor that he would be carrying on after all. But there are no second chances in the SAS. 'It would have been fine if he had kept his mouth shut and stopped being Tristan,' Peter said later. Tristan was out of the race, his dreams in ruins.

Elizabeth opened the door of her second-floor Queen's Gate flat later the same evening to a crestfallen boyfriend. Friends came round to cheer him up, and when it was decided to go out, Tristan jumped up on the narrow bannister rail to take a short cut by sliding down to ground level on his backside. He fell off and landed heavily on the concrete, splitting two fingers of his right hand like a spatchcocked chicken.

Elizabeth drove him to hospital, and after the wound had been stitched up, the invalid insisted on joining the others for dinner. Much later, in the early hours of a new day, Tristan told his girlfriend that his army days were numbered. It was time for something new.

CHAPTER FOUR

Sussex to Cape Town

THE WEEKS and months following Tristan's doomed attempt to join the SAS in 1981 are dismissed in his diaries with a line scrawled diagonally across each page, in recognition of a uniquely barren chapter in his life. Disappointed by his army experiences and without an academic qualification to fall back on, he joined the dole queue, but yearned for a life of adventure in Africa, which he knew to be a beguiling combination of few rules and many opportunities.

Weeks of inertia finally ended during an October evening at Folkington, where Tristan met the man he later claimed was responsible for his ultimate move to Africa. When Pearl invited Ian Hepburn – a family friend who had recently joined a land agency firm in Lewes – to dinner, she readily agreed to his suggestion that her youngest son might also enjoy meeting his work colleague, Ralph Crathorne. Not only had Ralph served in the SAS, he had just returned from a four-month solo motorbike ride from Cairo to Cape Town, an expedition undertaken as a last hurrah before settling down to a conventional job.

Tristan was captivated by the guest's African adventures and was excited to learn that the Honda XL250 trail bike would soon be arriving at Felixstowe docks. Ralph was so overwhelmed by Tristan's determination to emulate his own African journey that he left Folkington having sold him the bike he had intended to keep forever.

After the motorbike arrived in Sussex, Robin Knight Bruce, his friend from Sandhurst days who had raced Hondas in Australia before joining the army, came up from Devon to show Tristan the ropes. A morning spent purchasing essential spare parts in Hastings was followed by a couple of hours riding around on the South Downs, after which Tristan pronounced himself ready for Africa and suggested they retire for a drink. 'He just got on with it,' is how Robin remembers the only motorbike lesson Tristan ever took.

In those days, most adventurers on long road trips across Africa rode large, heavy bikes requiring a full licence, but the 250cc trail bike could be driven on learner plates and was light enough to pick up in the event of a tumble. Tough, reliable and compact, it was the perfect machine for someone with virtually no previous experience of motorbikes.

Tristan found a willing partner for his enterprise in Peter Bateman, who was equally frustrated to have failed the SAS selection and was also contemplating a future in Africa. The two had not seen each other since that fateful August day in the Brecon Beacons, but Tristan jumped at the opportunity to meet up again when Peter telephoned to propose dinner together in London. When Tristan divulged his plan to ride a motorbike from Sussex to Cape Town, Peter suggested they do the trip together, since he was also making arrangements of his own to travel overland from the UK to Botswana, where his mother was living in Francistown.

'We'd both travelled widely and knew how things were done,' Peter remembered many years later from his boatyard at Kilifi, overlooking the Indian Ocean. 'My father was in the army, and after my parents separated my mother had lived in Botswana, Kenya, Uganda and Zambia. We thrashed out a tentative plan over dinner; we'd go across Europe to Venice, catch the boat to Alexandria, go through Egypt to Lake Nasser, catch the ferry to Sudan and then follow the Nile south to Juba and then take it from there. The whole thing could have been written on the back of a packet of cigarettes.'

Early in the New Year, the travellers set about making their plans concrete by applying for visas, which in the case of Sudan meant acquiring a letter of introduction to accompany their application. A friend, whose family owned a trading business in Khartoum, wrote a letter for the benefit of the Sudanese authorities explaining the bearers were going to visit a business there on his behalf. They also had to obtain a Carnet de Passages en Douane from the AA before leaving home, the international customs document that would allow their motorbikes free passage through all of the countries they intended visiting except Uganda, which in 1982 was not a signatory to the agreement. Although the well-travelled young men were confident and worldly, they knew their proposed route would be taking them through countries such as Sudan, and later Uganda, which were politically unstable and potentially very dangerous.

Tristan was not going to let the adventure he had planned with Peter get in the way of a long-standing commitment to join friends in Kenya for Christmas. He spent Christmas Day enjoying game drives in the Masai Mara before sitting down to a traditional dinner, recording 'delicious roast turkey' in his diary, the first of many references he was to make when food was exceptional, home-grown or hunter-gathered.

The holiday continued with a visit to the sleepy tropical island of Lamu, where Tristan and Elizabeth had lunch with her godmother, Pamela (Pam) Scott, who was taking a Christmas break from Deloraine, the colonial mansion built in the 1920s on the edge of the Great Rift Valley by her settler father, Lord Francis Scott. Tristan knew that Pam had recently retired from running a successful farming enterprise at Deloraine, but could never have foreseen that his hostess lived in the house he would one day call home. Returning to a cold English winter after a fortnight in paradise was much easier than on any of his previous visits to Kenya; this time Tristan knew he would be back within a month.

Tristan's return to Africa in February 1982 was delayed after he called into the Woolpack Inn at Brookland, halfway between Folkington and Dover, for a quick drink with friends on his way to the ferry. A farewell pint dissolved into the inevitable drinking session, during which the ferry set sail as Peter Bateman waited in vain for his travelling companion to arrive at the terminal; they eventually boarded the Calais ferry twenty-four hours late on a grey and miserable morning.

A night in the French port held little appeal so they drove through the pelting rain to a YMCA hostel in Arras, wearing Barbour jackets to turn the weather. Conditions had still not improved when they reached Turin two days later via the Mont Blanc Tunnel through the Alps, too cold, wet and tired to appreciate an Italian city rich in history and culture.

Amends were made in Venice the following night, where the pair left their bikes in a multi-storey car park and joined revellers wearing fancy dress in Piazza San Marco, but not before Tristan had written postcards home to his family and friends. A lively evening ended with a search for somewhere to stay by gondola, although Tristan steadfastly refused all the gondolier's pricey recommendations and insisted on somewhere cheap and cheerful. 'Cheep, cheep, cheep, good night,' the boatman laughed, mimicking Tristan in broken English when taking his fare.

With ferry tickets booked for the next leg of their journey, there was no time to linger in Venice, and the following day they left on a protracted voyage to Egypt, steaming down the Adriatic Sea before entering the Gulf of Corinth through the narrow Corinth Canal. The boat docked in Athens for forty-eight hours, which allowed time to visit the mighty Parthenon, but the most interesting time there was spent drinking beer with a German travelling on a motorbike that had seen army service in the Second World War.

Landing at the Mediterranean port of Alexandria, two days after leaving Athens and the grand cities of Europe behind, felt like the real start of the adventure and arrival in another world. Spring sunshine and a fresh north breeze replaced the stormy weather that had beset their voyage across the Mediterranean, and the modern streets of a city founded by Alexander the Great were crammed with dark-skinned locals and scrawny donkeys wandering between lines of honking cars.

The motorbikes weaved their way slowly through heavy traffic onto the main road to Cairo and reached the Fontana Hotel in the heart of Ramses Square by late afternoon. Both travellers found it impossible to sleep until the unrelenting chorus of loud, blasting horns suddenly fell silent at 3.00 a.m., only to resume exactly an hour later. A visit to the shambolic Egyptian museum – in the throes of being rebuilt – was followed by a twilight excursion to the pyramids at Giza on the west bank of the Nile. An over-attentive guide there refused to leave the tourists alone, and when Tristan pushed him away with a flat hand to the chest, the Egyptian collapsed with the flamboyance of a diving footballer. This was cue for several hostile Arabs to appear from the surrounding shadows, and a hasty motorbike exit in a cloud of dust.

Bikes were loaded onto the overnight train from Cairo to Luxor three days later, and propped up in the walkway outside the sleeping compartment, as their owners tried to rest while the crowded train

ALEXANDRIA TO LAKE NASSER

MEDITERRANEAN SEA

ALEXANDRIA

CAIRO

SUEZ CANAL

THE NILE

EGYPT

VALLEY OF THE KINGS

LUXOR

EDFU

ASWAN

RED SEA

LAKE NASSER

SUDAN

followed the Nile south, arriving at Luxor in the middle of the night. The Holiday Home Hotel there was 'awful' according to Tristan's diary, but no one objected when he and Peter rode their bikes up the stairs and into their bedroom at 4.00 a.m.

Whilst in Luxor, they sailed across the Nile on a traditional felucca to visit the Valley of the Kings, but Tristan's mood changed abruptly when a guide presented him with a donkey to ride up to the ancient burial site. It was not the folded blanket masquerading as a saddle that he objected to, but the animal's poor condition and frailty. He refused to subject the donkey to his weight, but walked beside it instead, much to the astonishment of the locals, who had never seen a tourist leading a donkey before.

A long bike ride to Aswan on the north shore of Lake Nasser was broken by a night sleeping out beneath the stars in the desert south of Edfu, but the following day trouble in the form of an officious police officer ruined their visit to the southern Egyptian city. Peter was repairing a puncture when the police drove up, bundled both men into a car and drove them to the station, where they were interrogated separately under suspicion of being spies, before being left in the charge of an unsmiling armed guard.

At the end of a long day, during which all attempts at reason had failed, Tristan finally snapped. He grabbed the guard's rifle, deftly removed the magazine, hurled it onto the floor and sprinted down the stairs into the hot afternoon sun with Peter close behind. He had the good sense to leave the weapon behind, dropping it on the footwell on his way out of the door. The friends waited anxiously at the plush InterContinental Hotel that evening, half-expecting the police to come and arrest them, but no one of authority appeared and their last night in Aswan passed without incident.

Two nervous passengers hovered about the ferry terminal waiting to board the 1.00 p.m. departure for the 186-mile voyage across Lake Nasser the next morning, but their tension eased as Aswan shrank into a speck on the horizon, before disappearing into a blue void framed by dazzling yellow desert on either side of the lake. First class cabins had been booked for the voyage, but the travellers quickly realised they would be much more comfortable on the exposed upper deck than in a sweltering cabin, where their access was obstructed by luggage, boxes and people. The upper deck was crowded, too, especially when prayers were broadcast from the bridge, and rows of kneeling worshippers bowed their heads towards the shrine of Mecca five hundred miles to the east.

The boat docked on the bleak, rocky headland of Wadi Halfa in Sudan two days later, where the tortuously slow immigration process was eased by their letters of introduction. They were entering a country that had only recently completed three-month-long elections and was soon to be subjected to Gaafar Nimeiry's strict fundamentalist Islamic regime.

Against this backdrop, the Sudanese were beginning to hoard

diminishing stocks of petrol, but each motorbike had been modified to carry fuel for more than seven hundred miles, enabling the travellers to push on across the hot, empty landscape of the Nubian Desert. They drank from tin containers wrapped in hessian sacking to keep the water cool, which were stored in ammunition boxes strapped to the crash bar of Tristan's bike.

The pair were welcomed according to timeless convention by a friend of a friend at Khartoum on the confluence of the Blue and White Nile rivers. Peter Lindstrom's parents had farmed in Kenya, and the Lindstroms' comfortable town house was a huge contrast to the shabby lodgings that had been their lot since the InterContinental hotel in Aswan. Peter ran a petrochemicals company and arranged for the bikes to be re-supplied with fuel before taking his guests to visit a camel souk, where a festival of dancing dervishes was cut short by a thick cloud that obscured the moon and plunged the revellers into blackness. Moments later, they were enveloped by a cold, rushing wind and a maelstrom of stinging sand, as a desert haboob[8] engulfed the display, forcing dancers and spectators to flee for shelter.

With three nights of hospitality behind them, the bikers continued south, following the course of the White Nile to Kosti, where they were given food and lodgings by a missionary, and then on to camp at Rabak on the east bank of the Nile. A swarm of mosquitoes appeared at dusk, and within an hour the exterior of their tent was an inch deep with insects. The humming of a million hungry parasites became such an unbearable torment that they decided to drive on through the night, reaching Malakal after an exhausting thirteen hours on the road.

When they reached Nimule National Park several days later, a decision was made to continue the journey south through Uganda, rather than heading east into Kenya via Lake Turkana as Ralph Crathorne had done the previous year. Tristan had already visited the Jade Sea,[9] and was keen

---

8   A violent and oppressive wind blowing in summer in Sudan and elsewhere, bringing sand from the desert.

9   Another name for Lake Turkana on account of its turquoise colour caused by algae rising to the surface in calm weather.

WADI HALFA TO KAMPALA

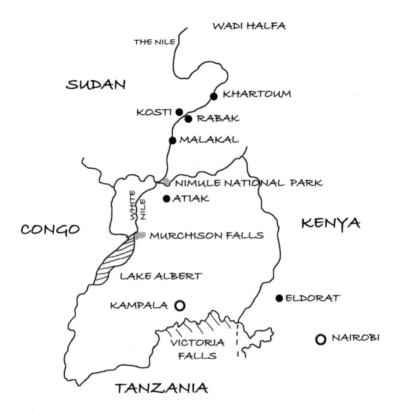

to explore Murchison Falls[10] and Lake Albert, despite the risks of taking a route that every sane traveller in Africa was avoiding after Milton Obote's election as president four months earlier. His victory was contested by Colonel Museveni and his supporters, who had retreated into the Luwero bush around Kampala to form the National Resistance Army, in preparation for a brutal civil war that over the next two years was to claim the lives of more than 100,000 civilians.

Tristan and Peter cleared immigration from Sudan into Uganda south of Nimule National Park with the help of forged papers stating their

---

10 Murchison Falls National Park, locally known as Kabalega Falls National Park, is situated at the end of the Albertine Rift Valley and is Uganda's oldest and largest safari park. It is located 305 kilometres north of Kampala.

Carnet de Passages was now recognised by the Ugandan authorities, and the bribe of packets of Knorr soup. Once in Uganda, the two pressed on to Atiak, where the chief of police agreed to let the white men stay in a rondavel[11] at the station. Tristan could think of nowhere safer than a police station, but the officer instructed them sternly, 'Do not leave your lodging after dark, there are lots of trigger-happy boys out there.'

They heeded his warning, but were woken in the middle of the night when their rondavel was raked by gunfire, following an incident that ended with the execution of an intruder. The walls of Paraa Safari Lodge in Murchison Falls National Park the next day were also riddled with bullet holes, but that did not diminish the enjoyment of the first cold beer since Khartoum and a chicken and rice dinner, although there were no eggs on offer for breakfast the following morning. 'You ate the hen last night,' explained the waiter.

They passed an abandoned tank on the roadside north of Kampala, and the following day were relieved to leave Uganda behind and enter the familiar landscape of Kenya, twenty miles north of Eldoret. After six weeks of relentless and uncomfortable travel, there was now time to relax amongst friends. Peter and Tristan went their own ways, Tristan heading to Rosslyn to visit his Elizabeth and Sonia Ryrie, and then onto the coast at Watamu, before the pair reconvened to climb Mount Kenya in early April.

Complications with entry papers for Tanzania and a shortage of motorbike spare parts then delayed the resumption of their journey by several days. As Peter was obliged to enter Tanzania a week later, and Tristan was already committed to joining some English friends on a pre-arranged layover in Zimbabwe, the assault on Mount Kenya marked the end of their adventures together. They did not see each other again until catching up in Johannesburg several months later, after which Peter found the work he had hoped for in Botswana.

Years later, the two were reunited when Peter called in to visit Tristan on his way from Nairobi to Kampala on business, and has fond memories of a 'wonderful night reminiscing' about their extraordinary motorbike journey twenty years earlier.

---

11 A traditional circular African dwelling with a conical thatched roof.

Tristan made sure he reached Zimbabwe by early May, in order to fulfil a long-standing commitment to meet with his friends Robin Knight Bruce and Martyn Lee, who had flown out from England to join him. Martyn and his entourage had been invited to join a white farming family in Zimbabwe for a few weeks of fun, which Tristan had been looking forward to since the start of his adventure. The Hensmans' farm at Braeside, near Sinoia,[12] was presided over by Colin Hensman senior, aka 'The Godfather', who had served with the Selous Scouts[13] and farmed there ever since his arrival on an ox train from South Africa between the wars.

His uncle had left him with a native helper, a roll of barbed wire, and instructions to cut out a farm. 'I'll be back in a year to see how you are getting on,' were his parting words. Braeside had since grown into a profitable mixed farm employing hundreds of local people, and a warm family home. Brothers Rory and Gary Hensman embraced the challenge of entertaining their visitors with enthusiasm, arranging bird shooting, polo matches and a camping trip to Lake Kariba.

The hosts also invited three young women to join them, and balmy afternoons were spent water-skiing and fishing on the farm's huge artificial dam, although catastrophe was narrowly averted when the steering wheel came off in Tristan's hands when he was driving the boat at high speed. By immediately killing the throttle and leaning over the side he prevented the vessel from ploughing headlong into the shore, and the occupants survived after a few heart-stopping seconds of real danger.

That evening Tristan recorded the day's events in his diary with unusual detail. 'All day on the dam skiing and fishing with Alison, Caroline and Sarah,' he wrote on 24th May 1982. 'Nearly killed when steering broke on the boat.' He didn't realise it at the time, but Tristan had just expended the first of his nine lives.

The farm was also home to an abundance of plains game, and Tristan

---

12 Sinoia in Zimbabwe, now called Chinhoyi.

13 Selous Scouts were a special forces regiment of the Rhodesian Army that operated from 1973 until the reconstitution of the country as Zimbabwe in 1980. Named after the British explorer Frederick Courteney Selous (1851–1917).

TRISTAN IN ZIMBABWE

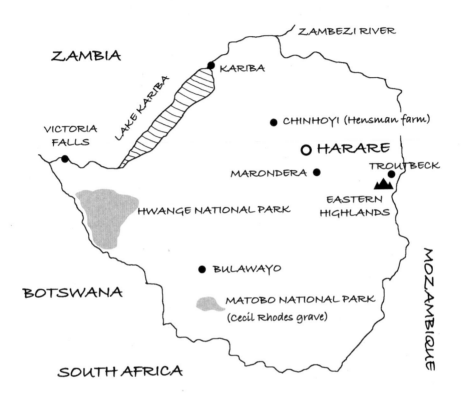

shot a cull sable antelope[14] early one morning, but decided against taking the horns home to Folkington, as he knew how much they would upset his dear mother. The friends were encouraged to use Braeside as a launch pad from which to explore Zimbabwe, and combined a trip to Victoria Falls in the Hensmans' borrowed Mercedes with a safari in Hwange National Park and a visit to Cecil Rhodes's grave in the Matobo Hills. They caught trout at an altitude of 6,500 feet in the Eastern Highlands and stayed with Mrs Whaley-Birch and her one-eared terrier (the other one had been chewed off by a leopard) at her Troutbeck home.

Tristan admired the Munnings print of the Belvoir foxhounds before dinner, but noticed a small round hole in the middle. 'That's

---

14 A cull animal is one considered suitable to be culled to improve the quality of the herd.

not from a weevil,' their hostess explained, 'it was made by a bullet.' The widow told her guests that she put a teapot over her head and hid beneath the bed whenever the property was attacked by insurgents from Mozambique.

The Hensmans' generous hospitality could not be prevailed on indefinitely, and the final dinner at Braeside on the last day of May was a poignant farewell to a family who would continue to inspire and entertain Tristan for the rest of his life. Rory Hensman remained a close friend, and later found fame for his work with elephants at Braeside, and ultimately the long, sad journey he was to make with twelve of them down to South Africa, after being forcibly removed from his farm by Robert Mugabe's government in 2002.

The party headed south for Salisbury the following day, where Tristan saw his friends off at the airport, and noticed workmen replacing signposts saying *Salisbury* with ones that read *Harare*. When Tristan entered South Africa a week later, he left behind a country that had made a deep impression, for the mood in Zimbabwe was buoyant and optimistic, despite the recent end of British rule. He had made new friends, seen incredible wildlife, and visited prosperous, well-run farms. On his motorbike journey south to Johannesburg, he decided Zimbabwe was now where his future lay, not Kenya.

Johannesburg felt strangely safe and secure at the end of Tristan's journey, but after five action-packed months on the road, during which every kind of challenge had been overcome, Tristan was in no mood for petty authority. He particularly objected to being denied entrance to a Johannesburg nightclub with Jeremy Mainwaring-Burton and his wife, Nicky, by sour-faced Afrikaners determined to enforce the dress code of no jeans. Never one to be beaten by unnecessary restrictions of any sort, Tristan cheekily asked Nicky if she could lend him the skirt concealed beneath her knee-length jersey. He removed his jeans and pulled the garment up around his waist, and since there was no rule against wearing skirts, the doormen waved him through.

Tristan eventually arrived in Cape Town at the end of July, but within a week was back in Zimbabwe on the hunt for a job. He found one managing a farm at Marondera, some seventy miles east of Harare, but was unable to take up the position after the government refused to grant him a work permit. Seven months after leaving home, Tristan's African adventure had run out of steam. The faithful Honda was sold in Harare, and on 1st September, he arrived back in England.

Thirty-two years later, Tristan re-established contact with Ralph Crathorne, who had continued to combine an adventurous life with practising as a land agent in Sussex, and thanked him for inspiring the bike ride that changed his life. Any doubts regarding the significance of Tristan's six-month journey through Africa were dispelled by the text he sent to Ralph in July 2014: 'My being in Africa is almost entirely due to meeting you at that juncture of life and having just left the army. I would never have got my act together or thought of that safari, had I not met you and been impressed by your journey.'

* CHAPTER FIVE *

No Going Back

BACK in England at the start of another hunting season, Tristan fell quickly into the familiar winter routine of hunting and shooting with friends from all over the UK, which left the spring and summer months for race meetings, weddings and long weekends at The Mill. He found temporary work in London and helped his former army colleague, Martin Horsford, with a building project in Battersea, but these were minor diversions compared to the freedom of life on the road in Africa.

Tony Church's offer of a job with Safaris Unlimited in Kenya towards the end of 1983 was the lifeline that Tristan had been waiting for. It offered a heady mix of adventure, wildlife and horses, in a country whose charms he had found impossible to resist.

After the challenges of his first riding safari, and the safe return of the runaway horses, it was something of a relief to spend a few weeks escorting guests from the Mara River Camp on day rides exploring the surrounding bush, although danger was never far away, and there are several references to close encounters with buffalo and other big game in Tristan's diaries.

The horses carried on escaping, too, although they were invariably rounded up with the help of the Maasai staff and Tristan's colleague, Liza Burrel, who carried a Colt .45 on her hip. After it was decided to tether the horses on a long line overnight, instead of keeping them inside an electric enclosure, they absconded much less frequently.

Employing Maasai such as Charles, Metian and William of Orange – named for his habit of always carrying an orange blanket – helped Safaris Unlimited to build a good relationship with their pastoralist hosts, who welcomed tourists in exchange for a reasonable fee. The local Maasai often helped locate runaway horses, and on at least one occasion corralled them safely overnight with their cattle, goats and sheep. Tristan was soon allowed to take his clients into a local village, where they could see how the Maasai lived in tiny, windowless mud-and-cattle-dung huts, surrounded by their precious livestock, with the open plains at their front door.

The visitors learnt how the tribespeople drank a mix of blood and milk from leather gourds, and on rare occasions were permitted to observe the male circumcision ceremony, which is a rite of passage into manhood. Teenagers who endure the three-minute operation without displaying any sign of pain are honoured and respected by their peers from that day on, but any young man who visibly flinches beneath the knife brings dishonour upon himself and his family for evermore. Tristan had to pay a small fee to attend these ritual ceremonies, and sometimes engendered further goodwill by purchasing sheep or goats for his clients' supper.

As it became clear that endurance rides were more profitable than shorter day rides, the longer and more adventurous safaris gradually increased, providing Tristan with the opportunity to impress Tony with his knowledge, enthusiasm and initiative.

'Safaris Unlimited's bookings were growing and Tristan was very much part of the team,' is how Tony Church later recalled this exciting era. 'He proved himself remarkably quickly.' He also appreciated Tristan's high standards and attention to detail, and was impressed by his carefully thought-out seating plans, and insistence on carving meat at the table. 'These were aspects of his military style,' Tony noted, 'but my own background was somewhat different.'

Tristan's duties included guiding overland vehicle safaris that encompassed such iconic destinations as Lakes Baringo and Bogoria, The Aberdares, Samburu Land, Tsavo, Mzima Springs and Lake Turkana in the north. These journeys through wondrous landscapes were rich in wildlife and adventure, with unusual sightings or experiences being recorded for posterity in his diaries.

There were sometimes opportunities to join new friends on reconnaissance trips further afield, such as an exploration of the Serengeti in Tanzania to assess potential campsites with Charlie and Mouse McConnell, where they witnessed a martial eagle carry off a newborn cheetah in its talons. Whenever time permitted, Tristan also worked as a freelance guide and driver for companies such as Abercrombie & Kent and Richard Bonham Safaris.

Against this backdrop, Tristan was given greater responsibility for the administrative side of organising safaris, which entailed regular trips to Nairobi. These often began with a farewell dinner for clients at the Carnivore Restaurant, before driving them to the international airport for late-night departures back to the USA or Britain. He would return to the airport a few days later to meet and collect the next party, often taking them to stay at the Norfolk Hotel, before the long drive west to the Masai Mara the following morning.

In the meantime, there were firearms procedures and bank business to attend to in town and supplies of food and camping equipment to purchase from the stores in Karen. He took on responsibility for drawing up safari inventories, and kept meticulous records of rates, terms of contract, prices and advertising costs.

Having passed his initiation working for Tony Church under the radar, Tristan needed a work permit to comply with the law and was described as an 'Equine Consultant' on Safaris Unlimited headed paper. The government's policy of Africanisation often led to long delays or even disappointment with applications, but much to everyone's surprise, Tristan's self-employed permit was quickly granted. As Tristan's visits to the capital city increased, so did a social life revolving around a young and glamorous group of expat friends, who shared his love of adventure and confidence in the future of a country they were determined to call home.

Elizabeth Ryrie had also returned to Kenya, where she taught cooking, catered for safari lodges and worked as a freelance designer for various films and commercials. The couple saw each other whenever possible, and, during Tristan's frequent visits to Rosslyn, her mother Sonia started to teach him Swahili, which he picked up remarkably quickly. Their expanding circle of close friends included Lonrho employee Bimb Theobald, auctioneer Roland Purcell and Lucy Vigne, whose family had been forced to flee the apartheid regime in South Africa, after her father publicly condemned their policies and became a member of the non-racial Liberal Party.

Tristan met Lucy for the first time at a Nairobi dinner party, although she had already admired his 'dashing good looks, shock of wavy brown hair, piercing blue eyes and attractive nose and hands' from a safari photograph shown to her by a mutual friend. The two argued furiously about South African politics that evening, but discovered shared concerns regarding overpopulation and poaching, which was especially relevant since Lucy had arrived in Kenya six months earlier and found work for the International Union for Conservation of Nature (IUCN).

'It was wonderful fun having such a heated argument with someone I had only just met,' Lucy remembered, 'and we became firm friends as a result. I loved Tristan's outspoken and passionate nature, even when we did not agree.'

Within three months of meeting Bimb Theobald, Tristan had accepted his new friend's invitation to share his house in the Nairobi suburb of Lavington whenever he was in town, together with a flexible rota of lodgers that included Lucy Vigne and a terrier called Bonkers. The Bunker – named on account of its unprepossessing appearance – became Tristan's Nairobi base and the venue for countless wild parties. The nondescript oblong bungalow stood beside a road lined with purple blossoming jacaranda trees, and was surrounded by plots of divided land and dogs that barked all night. Lucy met her future husband at a party there; Johnny Camm was a popular and charismatic polo-playing computer programmer, who quickly became one of Tristan's closest friends, and a staunch ally through good times and bad in the years ahead.

Wild parties were not confined to The Bunker, but frequently and spontaneously developed over boozy lunches or dinners at the Muthaiga Country Club and other colonial outposts around town. 'Chance meeting with Mark Macaulay and Michael Cecil degenerates into drunken lunch. All appointments to the wind,' is a typical diary entry for a time of Tristan's life when he manages to define inebriation with a remarkable lack of repetition. The many and varied descriptions include 'heroically drunk, pissed as newts, legless, rather drunk, very drunk, pitifully drunk, immense hangover, drunk and disorderly mostly, dreadful hangover, very festive' and 'plastered'.

On one occasion festivities began with lunch at the Norfolk Hotel and ended up twelve hours later with a drunken brawl on the Carnivore dance floor, described as 'get drunk to falling over. Eventually, having fought Macaulay, go home without him.' While these long drinking sessions sometimes ended badly, they also served as important think-tanks, where young friends could bounce ideas around and cement enduring friendships. Tristan would learn that in Africa, it helps to have as many friends as possible.

General letting down of hair and hard partying during visits to Nairobi provided an antidote to the dangers of life on safari in the bush, and the weighty responsibility for client safety. A few weeks after his first Christmas safari, Tristan took Tim and Belinda Hextall out for an early morning ride from Mara Bush Camp; Belinda was an accomplished horsewoman, but her husband had never ridden before. They followed the Mara River downstream, passing elegant giraffes and elephants noisily ripping down branches, when a bull buffalo that had been lying down 150 yards ahead of them suddenly stood up, dropped his head and charged without warning.

The three horses whipped round and bolted in terror, but the novice rider fell off and was dragged along by his foot for twenty or thirty yards before being released when the stirrup leather snapped in two. Tim lay still as the buffalo thundered on after his riderless horse, before eventually giving up pursuit and wandering off into the scrub. Years later, Tim recalled the life-threatening incident with remarkable sangfroid. 'Knowing Tristan's reputation,' he said, 'I thought that this sort of thing was a normal occurrence for him.'

Tim was very lucky that day. One of the renowned Big Five[15] game species coveted by hunters, Cape buffalo compete with Nile crocodile and hippopotami for the accolade of causing more human fatalities than any other animal in Africa. Herds of breeding cows and younger bulls can be approached on horseback in comparative safety, but the older bulls — nicknamed duggas[16] — value their privacy and hide out in small groups

---

15 In Africa, the Big Five game animals are the lion, leopard, rhinoceros (both black and white species), elephant, and Cape buffalo. The term 'Big Five' was coined by big-game hunters and refers to the five most dangerous and challenging animals in Africa to hunt on foot.

16 Meaning mud, a name given to the older male buffalo that have passed their prime breeding age and now spend much of their time at mud wallows.

amongst the thickest of acacia scrub.

Unpredictable, temperamental and aggressive, these reclusive males often charge without warning when disturbed. A human on two legs has little chance beneath the furious might of an animal weighing up to a ton, and horns that dip down from a hard boss before curving upwards and outwards to sharp polished tips. Cape buffalo are accorded a uniquely formidable status by big-game hunters, on account of their legendary hunger for vengeance. Tracking a wounded one through thick scrub is an incredibly dangerous exercise, as the hunter quickly becomes the quarry of a beast that is stealthy, fearless and utterly committed to the destruction of its enemy.

Although hunting buffalo for sport was outlawed in Kenya in 1973, Tristan had met enough professional hunters to be aware of the species' determination to kill when provoked and knew men who had been stuck up trees for hours whilst an enraged buffalo paced angrily beneath.

Tristan was to experience an even closer shave with buffalo during another early morning ride from Mara River Camp with a willowy young American called Lois Lux. As they were returning to camp following a ride along the Soit Ololol Escarpment, a solitary bull buffalo stepped out in front of the riders and charged without warning or provocation. For a few seconds it seemed as if they would gallop unscathed to safety, but when Lois's horse swerved violently to avoid colliding with a tree, she fell straight into the path of the bull, who hammered into her chest with the hard boss between his horns.

Seeing the riderless horse beside him, Tristan yanked his own mount to a halt and drove him straight towards the girl being shoved unceremoniously through the dirt. He leapt from his horse and ran at the aggressor, thrashing the thick black hide repeatedly with his whip until the animal turned on him instead, allowing the American to crawl into the safety of thick scrub. Tristan also backed into a tangle of thorns, so thick that the bull could only shake his huge horns in frustration and grunt angrily from behind a wet black nose.

Lois Lux sustained broken ribs in an attack that could easily have killed her, yet she did not blame her guide in any way and was remarkably philosophical in a letter to her Californian tour operators.

'I do recognise there is a certain amount of danger involved in a horseback riding safari in the bush,' she wrote in July 1984. 'I realise that there is always the possibility that a rogue wild animal could be about. I do not think that either the guide or I reacted in a careless fashion or could have done anything to prevent the attack. I am very glad we both survived with minimal injuries.' She signed off by stating that the safari was the most enjoyable vacation she had ever experienced, 'although I could have done without the Cape buffalo incident.' Lois later sought employment in Kenya and for a time found work as a nurse in Nairobi, where she occasionally bumped into the man that had once saved her life.

The risks of an overland safari were less obvious than the dangers of a riding safari, but they existed nevertheless. Tristan was driving Tony's Land Cruiser high above the eastern shore of Lake Bogoria two weeks after the buffalo incident, when the narrow and precipitous track suddenly collapsed beneath it, leaving the vehicle marooned on its side with the front wheels facing the sky. The passengers were able to extricate themselves from the Land Cruiser's precarious resting place, believing that it would tumble down a steep slope into the lake below at any moment.

On surveying the disaster from a position of safety, it was clear to all that they were lucky to have escaped serious injury or death. Tristan turned to a Swiss member of the group, and told him, 'A cat has nine lives.' But in the space of only fourteen days, Tristan had gone from eight lives down to six.

At the time of these adventures, Tristan's girlfriend, Elizabeth, was enjoying an extended safari of her own in the company of another man, travelling with David Hicks Beach from Nairobi to Cape Town. They spent a few days in Botswana's Okavango Delta, hiring a guide, basic camping equipment, and a canoe with which to explore the myriad of waterways surrounding Chief's Island.

After dinner one evening, Elizabeth rolled out her sleeping mat for another night under the stars and fell asleep within yards of the glowing embers. She woke in the dead of night to the peculiar sensation of being dragged by her left ankle, belly down along the ground whilst still in her sleeping bag, and realised to her horror that the long swishing tail she could see over her shoulder belonged to a lioness tugging her into the bush.

Elizabeth screamed and kicked out with her free foot, but the lioness merely tightened her grip and continued to drag her victim away from the fire, as David and the guide started to hurl burning logs at the intruder. After several terrifying seconds, Elizabeth slid slowly out of her sleeping bag, which remained firmly clamped between the lioness's jaws as she melted into the bush. The three spent the rest of the night huddled sleepless around the fire listening to lions roaring from the darkness, as Elizabeth's foot turned black and yellow from the bruising it had sustained. They found her sleeping bag some distance away at first light, chewed to shreds and covered in saliva. A week later, a young girl was mauled to death within half a mile of their campsite, and the lioness was shot dead.

The couple were reunited in Nairobi after Elizabeth's own long safari was over, but she had dwelt on her boyfriend's shortcomings during their three-month separation. She could see 'streaks of chauvinism and insensitivity to the fairer sex' and was becoming wary of an increasingly wandering eye. Elizabeth believed that Pearl Voorspuy was responsible for her favourite son's sometimes cavalier attitude to women, which Tristan accepted and understood. 'She ruined us all,' he once joked, 'especially me.'

Elizabeth found Tristan 'wasn't hugely capable of love, but of great friendship,' admired his generosity, sense of fun and infectious giggles, but was sometimes frustrated by high-handedness and a lack of tolerance. Tristan liked to admonish anyone who added a comment to the visitors' book at Rosslyn, branding it a 'common' habit, but Elizabeth believed the real commonness lay in making the unfortunate recipient feel uncomfortable. 'It's common to bang on about being common,' she told him.

One morning over breakfast, the two agreed to end their six-year-long relationship, but Tristan was always welcome at Rosslyn, and remained close friends with Elizabeth for the rest of his life.

✤ CHAPTER SIX ✤

An African Romance

DIRECTOR Sydney Pollack's decision to shoot his epic romantic drama *Out of Africa*, on location in Kenya during the first six months of 1985, was to have far-reaching consequences for Tristan, for the success of the Oscar-winning film gave Kenyan tourism a boost that sustained everyone in the business for years afterwards. Tony Church's horses were hired for the equine scenes and Tristan was put in charge of training them to pull carts and buggies, during which he drew on childhood experiences with a pony and trap in Sussex. All the horses, oxen and mules used in the film boarded at Anthill, Tony's headquarters off the Langata Road, which were conveniently located opposite an enormous film set built to recreate early twentieth-century Nairobi.

Some of the livestock had also been supplied by Jackie Kenyon, whose Mogwooni cattle ranching property in Laikipia County, 250 miles north of Nairobi, was in the grips of such a severe drought that he needed to find work away from home; and his animals were guaranteed survival while occupied with the film. They were joined by his friend Charlie McConnell, a safari consultant, who was hired by Tristan to work as an extra on the film between hosting clients on safari.

Patience was tested during driving scenes that sometimes required numerous takes before the director was satisfied; these included the victory parade scene, which featured Tristan as an extra and had to be filmed on three consecutive nights. By the time their work was complete on a project described by Jackie as 'enormous fun', the three had become close friends, whose paths were destined to cross frequently in the years ahead.

During the early weeks of filming, a glamorous twenty-one-year-old horsewoman called Lucinda (Cindy) Macintosh arrived in Nairobi to recuperate from an accident sustained in England while team chasing, a cross-country contest at steeplechasing pace, but over bigger and hairier fences. As a young man, her father had walked and hitch-hiked his way across Africa from Tangier to the 60,000-acre Solio Ranch between The Aberdares and Mount Kenya to take up the offer of an assistant farm manager's job. Brian Macintosh later moved on to manage the Lewa Downs Ranch in Laikipia for David Craig,[17] and while there, he met and married Angela Beechener, who was working as a nanny for the American consul in Nairobi.

The couple returned to the UK in 1964 and ended up running a farm in Gloucestershire where Cindy was able to indulge her passion for racing, team chasing and hunting with the Heythrop. Her bravery, style and lithe good looks had already won her many admirers back in England, and given her close connections to Kenya, it was never a case of if she would meet Tristan, but when.

The inevitable encounter took place in early March, when Tristan strode into the Nairobi Polo Club during a break from filming and knocked over a pair of crutches that had been propping up the bar. 'Whose are these?' demanded the suntanned young man of military bearing. A slim girl spoke up from a table behind him. 'They're mine,' she said quietly, 'I've broken my pelvis.' Tristan spun round and glared at the culprit. 'Well, that was pretty careless of you,' he barked. Then, as his eyes took in the attractive young woman, he smiled an apology and softened. 'You'd better have a drink,' he said.

Two weeks later, Tristan invited his new friend to join him and four others on a short reconnaissance trip to the remote Tana River Delta, where Charlie McConnell and Terry O'Meara were in the process of establishing a safari camp that became Delta Dunes Lodge. As Cindy was only just out of crutches, Tristan added an unnecessary rider to his invitation: 'You can only come along provided you don't whinge.'

---

17 David Craig was a key figure in the development of what is now the Lewa Wildlife Conservancy, which combines conservation work with responsible tourism.

The Tana Delta concept was that clients, tents, staff and food would access a camp overlooking the Indian Ocean between Malindi and Lamu on board the *African Queen*, a thirty-foot-long trawler equipped with a propeller that Terry had fabricated from pieces of steel collected from a scrapyard. The engineering genius later excavated a well in the sand dunes, building up an ever-increasing collar of clay bricks that he allowed to slide down around him as he dug his way ever deeper to discover fresh water, without which the lodge could not function. Thanks to Terry's ingenuity, almost everything at the camp in those days was ancient and homemade, much of it succumbing to rust, rot and termites in a constant battle for survival.

When the small group arrived at their first campsite beside the Tana River, Terry leapt into the crocodile-infested waters to escape a plague of mosquitoes, whilst the others put up the tents. Cindy, who had not complained once during the thirteen-hour-long drive, noticed that there were only three tents and asked which was hers. 'You can sleep in mine if you want,' Tristan replied.

By the time the trip was over, Tristan and Cindy were very much closer, having shared all kinds of adventures in a river teeming with hippos and crocodiles, surrounded by bush that was home to large herds of buffalo, topi and zebra, as well as warthogs, giraffe and elephant. Terry's homemade propeller falling off on the second day only added to the excitement, as all the provisions had to be unloaded and stowed away on a much smaller vessel for the voyage to continue downstream.

'All day exploring. Absolute bliss,' Tristan wrote at the end of the following day. After the Tana River trip, Cindy's name crops up frequently in his diaries, and later that year she was invited to Folkington during one of his biannual visits to England, which were timed to coincide with Kenya's rainy seasons in April and November. Anxious to impress her new boyfriend's parents and unaware of their productive kitchen garden, Cindy arrived with a box of violet creams and a bunch of fresh asparagus, only to be admonished by Tristan for taking coals to Newcastle.

The rest of the visit was given over to London dinner parties, relaxing at The Mill, and catching up with old friends. At this stage of Tristan's life, there were stag nights and weddings to attend during his short visits to

England, including the marriage of his close expat friends, Johnny and Lucy Camm. 'Lucy very pretty,' he noted after the event.

Back on set in Nairobi, Tristan struck up a friendship with the actor Michael Kitchen, which led to Tristan taking him on a week-long riding safari in the Masai Mara. Michael was accompanied by his girlfriend, the actress Joanna Lumley, who later recounted her African adventures with Tristan in a magazine article.

She described the extraordinary wildlife, the comforts of camp, and the vast stretches of wild Africa, where huge horizons 'trick you into believing that you can see the curvature of the earth,' and with reference to his buffalo encounter the previous year, introduced Tristan as 'The man who knows no fear'.

Towards the end of the ride, they swam a flooded Mara River to avoid a seven-mile detour, with Tristan going first to show how it should be done. As his horse plunged into the brown torrent, a lioness appeared on the far bank and 'sank into a crouching position as breakfast swam towards her.' The rumble of a river in spate drowned out the onlookers' shouts of warning, but the lion retreated before Tristan reached the far bank, and the safari continued to Kichwa Tembo Camp.

Mara River crossings were to become a riding safari highlight in the years ahead and an ordeal or delight for many hundreds of clients. Joanna Lumley ended her article by urging her readers to visit the Masai Mara, but to 'try and get Tristan Voorspuy to take you.'

With the filming over, it was back to life as a (now paid) safari guide and more overland trips that did not feature horses at all. Tristan recorded the wildlife seen on game drives and riding safaris in his Smythson diaries, as meticulously as a sportsman completing a game book. There are 'good lion grunts and two buffalo' in the Northern Matthews Range, and a moonlit lion wandering through Kitich Camp at four in the morning. A kudu cow and her calf were spotted at Bogoria, and a pack of thirty wild dogs were encountered in the Mara, where cheetahs finally killed an impala after nearly four hours' pursuit. An elusive leopard was seen from horseback for the first time, another was spotted curled-up asleep in a bird's nest, and a pair were surprised mating on the plains.

Tristan got hopelessly lost picking raspberries, while climbing the third-highest peak of Mount Kenya in November 1985: 'Get back to camp at 7.30 p.m. after awful descent.' There are examples of compassion, too; three orphaned baby warthogs rescued with Charlie and Mouse McConnell and taken to nearby Little Governors' Camp for safe keeping, followed up by a second visit to check they were alive and well.

The diaries mention honeymoon lions, copulating hippos, twenty swimming elephants (underlined) in Meru National Park, a giant forest hog in The Aberdares, and an 'ostrich nest with 23 eggs attended by vultures' in the Mara. Leopard, lion, some two hundred buffalo and six hundred elephant are all seen during a single day from Tarangire tented camp in Tanzania. He catches a six-foot-long python in Lake Nakuru National Park and back in Meru, is chased by a twelve-foot-long crocodile guarding her eggs.

In December 1987, Tristan and Cindy Macintosh visited Kigali National Park in Rwanda, where their friend, Roland Purcell, had turned his back on auctioneering and was now living in a tree house in the Virunga Mountains, where he worked as a warden. After a long trek into the hills, Tristan was rewarded by a 'lovely hour with gorillas.'

Unsurprisingly, things did not always go according to plan. Vehicles often broke down or got bogged in wet weather, Nairobi lunches overran with dire consequences, and nights were sometimes spent on the back seat of a car. Horses continued to test patience and resources by running away from camp, and were targeted by hungry lions, usually at night but occasionally in broad daylight.

Clients frequently fell off and hurt themselves: concussion, a smashed-up face and broken bones are all considered worthy of mention. Two lady riders went missing during an afternoon ride in the Mara, but were discovered safe and sound before nightfall. An attempt to cross a swollen Mara River in August 1988 nearly ended in disaster, with only four riders reaching the far bank; the rest turned back and were collected at a bridge several miles upstream. 'Very lucky,' Tristan noted. 'Late arrival in camp rather tired.'

There were occasional run-ins with disgruntled Maasai, the odd minor robbery, and an argument that was nearly settled with a rungu,[18] after Tristan lost his temper with an African member of staff. In August 1988, three cow elephants charged a vehicle full of French clients during a game drive on Rhino Ridge in the Mara, described by Tristan as, 'Screaming French and car won't start.' The elephants stopped short of the Land Cruiser, which spluttered to life before they could change their minds. 'Write Cindy' that evening, underlined. Also in the Mara, riders were charged by a rhino and heard a second one 'snorting in the bushes', and nine lions were chased off by vehicles after wandering into camp during dinner.

Although surrounded by thriving wildlife, Tristan was also saddened and frustrated by constant evidence of poaching on his travels throughout Eastern Africa and he knew the terrible statistics. His early years guiding coincided with a drop in the Kenyan elephant population from 65,000 head in 1979, to 19,000 ten years later, a loss of some 46,000 lives in a single decade. The Kenyan black rhino population fared no better, plummeting by thirty per cent in just four years from 1984. Although hunting had been banned in Kenya since 1973, the trade in ivory remained legal, and poaching was well-established and flourishing there by the time Tristan arrived to work for Tony Church. A 1989 report in the *New York Times* labelled Kenya's Tsavo National Park as an elephant graveyard, and described the once-perfect pachyderm habitat as a landscape littered with piles of bleached white bones.

After the paleoanthropologist and conservationist, Richard Leakey, was appointed to head up the forerunner of the current Kenya Wildlife Service (KWS) in 1989, he famously consigned twelve tons of confiscated ivory to flames, rather than sell it to fund the conservation effort. The pyre was lit by the president, Daniel arap Moi, on 18th July and took more than three days to burn out, by which time images of the event had circulated around the world. The ivory bonfire contributed in part to the ban on ivory trade imposed by the Convention on International

18 A wooden throwing club or baton bearing special symbolism and significance in certain East African tribal cultures. It is especially associated with Maasai morans (male warriors), who have traditionally used it in warfare and for hunting.

Trade in Endangered Species (CITES) the following year, but during the course of Tristan's life at least another 117 tons of Kenyan ivory were to be destroyed the same way.

During the 1980s, it was impossible for any East African guide to avoid the ongoing slaughter of wildlife. Although Tristan noted with some satisfaction that poachers were caught on the Siria Escarpment above Kichwa Tembo in October 1985, he later records disappointing game drives on Meru's eastern border, with elephants 'very windy' and poaching suspected. On another visit to Meru, he spotted a young elephant limping in pain with a bullet hole through the leg and drove straight to the park headquarters to report his finding to a warden. Elephants in Tarangire were clearly frightened during a visit there in 1986, and the ground was littered with the bleached skulls of many that had been poached.

Even the famous wildlife sanctuary of the Ngorongoro Crater in Tanzania was not immune; remains of a slaughtered rhino were found there during a visit in October 1986, and a local guide revealed that two elephants had been killed by poachers only the previous week. Tristan watched more than two hundred elephants browsing peacefully below Gibbs Farm a month later, but was horrified to discover tusk ends for sale at the nearby Lake Manyara Hotel, and to spot rangers carrying ivory to a waiting car.

Back in the Mara, shots were heard during an early morning ride in 1987, followed by eighty frightened elephants coming off the hill; on their way back to camp the group passed a freshly killed giraffe. In September the same year, he stumbled across twenty zebra and a single giraffe butchered by poachers, but there was also hope. Tristan wrote 'very encouraging' after finding a herd of 300 elephants driving through Tsavo, but he wished there was more he could do to help safeguard Africa's wildlife.

Tristan was learning fast and making the Kenyan landscape his own, during a halcyon era unconstrained by the responsibilities of running a business or looking after anyone but himself. Going into his second year as a professional guide for Safaris Unlimited, he could name and identify nearly every East African bird, but always carried a guide book just in case. As his guests looked on, Tristan revealed the habits of the bird or animal they were watching, how elephants move silently across rocky ground, why the droppings of a hyena are brilliant white, and the cruel customs of the honeyguide bird.

He learnt how to read tracks like a Maasai and where to find different species of wildlife, imparting his knowledge generously and enthusiastically to clients, but had little patience for those who failed to pay attention, and an aversion to any form of squeamish behaviour. A safari guest from this era remembers being too frightened to ask Tristan to distinguish between a lilac-breasted roller bird and a pale chanting goshawk, and Lucy Vigne was admonished after expressing dismay over an impala's suffering at the teeth of cheetah cubs.

In perhaps the clearest statement yet of his intention to remain in Kenya, Tristan purchased a Border Terrier puppy, named him Bertie, and took him on safari when he was only a few months' old. Cindy was also a semi-permanent fixture by 1987, and on New Year's Day she won a race at the Limuru meeting, following in the footsteps of her mother, who had been successful at the same track when pregnant in 1963.

Encouraged by his friend Johnny Camm, Tristan resumed a polo-playing career that had begun in the army, and bought his first ponies, Njuguna and Tangul Bai, which were stabled at Nairobi polo ground before moving to board with Johnny. He also enjoyed his first day's hunting in Kenya with Ginger Bell's pack of drag hounds, which were kennelled in the Rift Valley near Nakuru, and began to take a close interest in the fortunes of the hunt.

By the end of that year, Cindy was driving Land Rovers, helping out on safaris, and providing hospitality to Tristan's friends at a house provided by Tony Church called The Roost. When Tristan was woken by a telephone call in the middle of the night with the news of his mother's death in February 1988, he flew back to England, but left Cindy in charge of the safari he was guiding. The funeral at Folkington was attended by 250 people and lasted all day. 'Very beautiful with garden looking lovely, snowdrops etc.,' wrote her youngest son. 'A lovely send off for poor mother.'

He was back after a fleeting visit to find the safari had progressed smoothly in his absence, but there were still long periods apart when Cindy returned to her racing job in Gloucestershire. After she flew out to Kenya in November 1988 and organised three back-to-back dinner parties, there was chat about 'what if I did this, what if I did that,' at which point Tristan countered, 'and what if I asked you to marry me?'

'That depends where, and when, and how you ask me,' Cindy replied.

'I'm asking you now.'

Cindy recalled her godmother's advice that if you need to think about a marriage proposal, you shouldn't do it, and promptly accepted.

As the venue for his stag night, Tristan chose the Muthaiga Country Club, which had become a favourite watering hole in Nairobi, and was also close to Rosslyn. The club's expat founders in 1913 included the Hon. Berkeley Cole, whose brother-in-law, Lord Delamere, persuaded several well-heeled friends to join him in Kenya as farmer settlers.

Many moved to the Wanjohi Valley near The Aberdares, where wild and promiscuous conduct earned them the epithet 'The Happy Valley Set', and when in town they all drank and dined at the Muthaiga Club. The close-knit group of friends were said to have 'drank champagne and pink gin for breakfast, played cards, danced through the night, and generally woke up with someone else's spouse in the morning.'

There had been many seismic political and cultural changes to Kenya since the 1930s heyday of wild behaviour, including independence in 1963; however, the private members' club on the evening of Tristan's stag night was still a small outpost of colonial Africa. Like-minded friends could relax there in comfort surrounded by gleaming parquet floors, masculine, leather-backed benches, and Munnings hunting prints on the walls.

There was, and still is, the head of a stuffed lion prominently displayed with the legend, 'Shot by Freddie Ward on Jan 27th 1905', which is reputed to have been used as target practice by high-spirited members long ago. Green, sun-drenched gardens lie beyond a shady terrace, where the tables are adorned with vases of fresh roses and starched white napkins. Women have been accepted as voting members since 2015, but a woman walking through the men-only bar two years later was still subjected to hisses of disapproval.

Tristan's stag night was a black-tie event that got underway with dinner for twenty close friends in the midnight-blue private dining-room, and ended in the small hours at the notorious Nairobi nightspot of New Florida. In-between there were all kinds of high jinks, mostly concerning two horses that Tony Church, Johnny Camm and Roland Purcell unloaded under the cover of darkness outside the west wing, just as the port was being passed around inside.

Members looked on in disbelief as Johnny and Roland rode Tony's horses bareback into the reception, in a high-spirited display that evoked memories of Lord Delamere riding his own horse into the Norfolk Hotel five decades earlier. Tristan was legged-up onto one of them and the polished floors were soon covered in piles of steaming manure, as the horses skidded about in chaos and guests sprayed fire-extinguisher foam all over the walls.

The party continued outside, where teams competed in a bizarre skiing relay, in which horses towed participants clinging onto their tails the full length of the car park. By the time the horsey part of the evening was over, many of the guests had sustained minor injuries, ruined leather shoes and ripped their clothes. Richard Bonham was bleeding so profusely from a head wound that the New Florida bouncers refused to let him in, whereupon he vanished into the night, only to resurface at the McConnells' house the following morning wearing a freshly laundered shirt and a big grin. The Spanish ambassador arrived at the club for breakfast about the same time and was not amused by random piles of horse droppings littering the reception floor.

There was considerable fall-out in the wake of what one participant described as 'the last great Muthaiga escapade' and threats to ban those responsible for the mayhem, including Johnny Camm, whose wife, Lucy, composed a letter for him to sign pleading clemency. Threats to impose huge fines were eventually forgotten, but Tony Church wrote a detailed account of the evening that was locked away in a time capsule after the club's centenary celebrations in 2013 and cannot be opened for another hundred years.

Today visitors browsing cartoons that line the wall of a corridor in the Muthaiga Club will find a framed sketch, entitled 'Tony Church *et al* ride into the front hall for a dressage lesson at Tristan Voorspuy's stag night', hanging alongside depictions of other celebrated events in the club's illustrious history. These include, 'Lady Delamere attracts the attention of the Prince of Wales' and 'Lady Beryl Markham arrives at the club for her regular Sunday lunch on August 1st 1982'. Tristan's own account is typically understated. 'My stag night at Muthaiga,' he wrote in his diary, 'horses and very drunken.'

Tristan had recovered sufficiently to attend a second stag night in Devon a few weeks later, which was organised by his best man and childhood friend, Martyn Lee. The evening again began with a civilised black-tie dinner – this time at the exclusive Highbullen Hotel near Umberleigh – after which an exasperated waitress attempted to throw a bucket of dirty water at her tormentors and ended up tipping the contents over her own head.

The evening wound up at The Mill nearby and exactly one week later, at 3.00 p.m. on 20th May 1989, Tristan and Cindy were married in the church at Folkington. Tristan and his ushers enjoyed a liquid breakfast nearby, which may have accounted for his fit of irrepressible, shoulder-shaking giggles, after a friend, Leigh Cranswick, brushed past him in the church and whispered in his ear, 'It's never too late to bail out.'

There was only room for half of the two hundred and fifty guests to watch Brian Macintosh give his daughter away inside the tiny church, which was bedecked in white lilies, daisies, stocks and delphiniums from Covent Garden. After the service, the congregation were joined by the other guests for a champagne reception in the beautiful garden at Folkington, which had been lovingly prepared for the event by Miss Coventry. On one of the hottest days of the year, many forsook the large marquee in favour of sunny lawns, where thick tail-coats were discarded in the sweltering heat.

Martyn Lee began his best-man's speech by cracking a well-received joke, and ended by reminding guests that the men in his Blues and Royals troop would follow their leader anywhere – 'if only out of curiosity'. Afterwards the married couple headed off in his brother Morven's open-topped Land Rover to give the elderly guests a chance to depart, but returned an hour later for a party that continued into the small hours.

The couple arrived back in Kenya to polo, safaris and a spectacular joint celebratory party with Johnny and Lucy Camm in August, but waited until November for a honeymoon on the Zambezi River with Tristan's good friend Garth Thompson as their guide. The holiday included a stay with Rory Hensman at Braeside near Chinhoyi, and Tristan was back in

Zimbabwe to try and negotiate the purchase of a farm there early the following year.

By 1986, the landlocked southern African country had been independent for six years under the rule of Robert Mugabe's Zanu Party, and although there was some unrest in the western Matabeleland region, there was little sign of the troubles that lay around the corner. Tristan had witnessed the success of the Hensmans' farm first hand and recognised Zimbabwe as a country where an agricultural enterprise could prosper. On a personal level, marriage to Cindy represented a watershed between a formerly carefree and poorly remunerated life and one where he must start earning a proper living.

When the farm sale fell through, Tristan decided that after two failed attempts to make a home in Zimbabwe, it was time to throw in his lot with Kenya. He loved the safari life there but sensed his position as a hired hand was drawing to a close, and the time was now right to discuss his future at Safaris Unlimited with Tony Church.

* CHAPTER SEVEN *

A Parting of the Ways

TRISTAN had been appointed a director of Safaris Unlimited by the time of his marriage but was also subcontracting Tony Church's horses and equipment to take his own clients on safari, in an arrangement that benefited both parties. Juggling his position as Tony's trusted head guide with his private safari enterprises kept Tristan busy, but he made time to buy up his own tents, horses and equipment whenever funds permitted, gradually becoming self-sufficient and less reliant on hiring from others.

Many of these private safaris were pulled together by Tristan's wide circle of English friends and family, such as the three-day-event rider, Lucinda Green, and his sister, Sorrel, by now married to banker Ed Woods. There was a particularly flamboyant safari over Christmas 1990 for twenty-six participants, which meant hiring even more tents and horses than Tony could supply, as well as an ex-army Bedford four-wheel-drive truck. On Christmas Day, guests broke their long morning ride with a huge picnic on top of the Siria Escarpment, and later watched three bull buffalo saunter past them at dusk.

In order to trade independently, Tristan arranged for Rupert Watson, a Nairobi-based lawyer originally from northern England, to register the name of his business as Offbeat Safaris, seven months after his marriage in 1989. Rupert brought the advantage of Kenyan citizenship to the party, and Tristan's close friend, Johnny Camm, joined the team as a third director. Early meetings were held at Rupert's Nairobi home, and are remembered by the lawyer for Johnny's practicality and Tristan's surprising ability to attend to the paperwork in a timely fashion.

Rupert was also impressed by Tristan's refined good manners, typified by his courteous habit of asking every lady seated at his table to dance at a party, and his handwritten thank-you letters signed 'with love', instead of a more formal ending. 'Everyone bangs on about how gung-ho Tristan was in those days,' he remembers, 'but he was actually soft in the middle and incredibly well-mannered, which contrasted with some of his right-wing views.'

In September 1990, Tristan was offered the chance to participate in another filming adventure, with the French journalist and environmental activist, Nicolas Hulot, who presented the television programme, *Ushuaïa, le magazine de l'extrême*, for the French television channel, TF1. The programme focused on extreme sport in wild landscapes throughout the world and Hulot – later France's Minister of Ecological and Inclusive Transition – was keen to add riding with African wildlife to a repertoire that included paragliding, skiing and rallying.

The first few days of filming in the Mara did not go according to plan, as the wildebeest were skittish and the presenter was not an accomplished rider, but the team ended up with some superb footage nonetheless. In a scenario that reminded Tristan of his harrowing ride through the dark back in 1983, the Voorspuys had to leave campsite in the pitch black early one morning to arrive at the Mara River in time for a sunrise shoot, where the film included a backdrop of grunting hippo.

By the end of the week, the crew had added a mock elephant charge, and an incredible sunset procession of giraffe, wildebeest and buffalo, cantering past the riders in a cloud of glittering dust. Some of the film clips were given to Tristan, and later spliced together to make the first Offbeat Safaris promotional video.

Tristan was well aware how beguiling and beautiful Kenya could appear in film, but he also understood the need to network and market his infant safari business overseas. With this in mind, he and Cindy travelled to the USA a month after filming for *Ushuaïa* had been completed, on the first of many promotional trips around the world. They could not resist stopping off in Dorset *en route* for a day with the Cattistock Hunt and Martyn Lee's birthday party but arrived in New York in time for a presentation on Offbeat Safaris at the Yale Club in midtown Manhattan.

They moved on to stay near Philadelphia with racehorse breeders Marshall and Bettina Jenny, whom Tristan had met on a previous Offbeat safari. During their stay, Marshall flew Tristan in his light aircraft over the Kentucky Derby winner, Northern Dancer, grazing peacefully in his paddock at Windfields Farm in Maryland, just ten days before the legendary stallion's death.

They also attended a meet of Mr Stewart's Cheshire hounds, where Tristan was thrilled to holloa a fox away from Runnymede covert, and mingled with American racing royalty before heading on to Virginia. Tristan was involved in an unfortunate accident there, when he forgot to drive on the right-hand side of the road on his way to meet friends for dinner in Middleburg. He leapt out of the car to see how the other driver had fared in the resultant head-on collision, helped him into an ambulance, and then spent two hours persuading the sheriff not to arrest him.

It was not until much later the same evening that Tristan's increasing discomfort resulted in his own visit to hospital, where he commiserated with the other driver after being diagnosed with a dislocated shoulder. Tristan was discharged from hospital in time to attend the Orange County Hunt breakfast the following day, where the guests included Jackie Onassis, although he was unable to persuade her to join an Offbeat safari.

There were more hunting and racing excursions, including a visit to Camden for the Colonial Cup in South Carolina, before the Voorspuys' three-week tour of the USA ended. They flew back to Kenya having made new friends and met numerous prospective clients from the American racing and hunting elite, a market that Offbeat was to capture convincingly in the years ahead.

The Voorspuys did not have time to visit the tour operators Bayard and Mel Fox at their Bitterroot Ranch in Wyoming during their American trip, but Equitours' patronage of Safaris Unlimited had grown since the success of *Out of Africa*, and their travel company was now Tony Church's principal client. Bayard and Mel often accompanied their clients on safari during the northern hemisphere winter, and their respect for Tristan and his guiding capabilities had strengthened with every visit. However, not everyone appreciated a guide who was increasingly pushing the boundaries. Those who rode bravely and well – typically British customers who had been brought up hunting and racing like Tristan – found fast gallops and close shaves with big game exhilarating, and refreshingly free from onerous safety regulations back home.

In recent years, however, some clients had criticised their guide for what they viewed as reckless and irresponsible behaviour, and penned bitter letters of complaint. An art dealer from Boston, Massachusetts, was so dissatisfied by his experiences with Tristan in January 1988 that he wrote Tony Church a four-page letter of protest, despite having enjoyed some magical wildlife sightings during his safari that included a pride of twenty-three lion and a bitch cheetah with cubs. The American condemned his guide as 'rude, negative, self-centred, discourteous, immature, reckless, and discriminatory towards elder members of the group,' but noted that Tristan was 'much more accommodating to the younger and prettier girls.'

The client took particular exception to an incident when the group of fifteen riders were chased by an elephant, which he claimed Tristan had provoked into charging. 'His stupid, so-called courage in getting so close to a cow elephant with calves has caused him a disfigured face with black-and-blue bumps and bruises,' the complainant wrote from his Boston office a week later. 'He could have lost his head, I could have lost mine, or any other member of the group could have been injured beyond immediate repair. When the horses ran off in all different directions, the riders could only say 'Hail Mary' and hope that he or she would come out of it in one piece.'

The writer also objected to his guide's lack of patience and information, disregard for nervous riders, and general high-handedness, and ended by making an oblique reference to *Out of Africa*. 'If he wanted to show off to the younger girls by playing Robert Redford, he should have selected an acting career and gone to Hollywood.' Tristan's diary note of the elephant charge is characteristically less melodramatic: 'Brandy takes me through a tree for 2 black eyes,' he wrote.

On another occasion, Tony Church received a strongly worded letter from the CEO of the Kenyan Association of Tour Operators (KATO), enclosing a complaint from an American senator, who had been on safari at Governors' Camp and encountered 'a white cowboy chasing game with a bunch of wild horsemen in the Koyiaki Group Ranch.'[19] Tristan was asked to compose a written apology, but could not resist adding a jibe about game needing to be kept on its toes, in order to reduce vulnerability to predators.

Incidents such as this were making Tony increasingly nervous of how his guide's forthright style might affect his business. 'I could see Tristan was a wild character, and I was cautious about accidents, because a serious one would be a real blow to the whole concept of riding safaris,' Tony recalled. 'He was having a thoroughly good time at my expense; I had the framework and he was imprinting his character and his daring lifestyle onto the rides, which I liked and admired in many ways, but I am fifteen years older, and had a family to provide for with little capital to fall back on.'

Against this backdrop there was also a steady deterioration in Bayard and Mel Fox's relationship with Tony Church, for they disliked economies such as rationing breakfast sausages and charging clients for drinks. 'If the damned safari was costing 5,000 dollars,' Bayard recalled, 'to charge someone fifty bucks more for their drinks didn't appeal to either of us.' They were also upset to discover a competitor in the travel business had been given lower rates than the ones they had agreed with Safaris Unlimited.

Tony had his own, equally bitter grievances against Equitours regarding slow payment of bills, and what he suspected was a plot to secure the exclusive services of Tristan in a clean break from his own company. Although Tristan declined Bayard's offers of financial help, he was aware that repeat Equitours clients were demanding his services as their guide. The Voorspuys had firmly committed to a joint future in Africa, and Tristan would have liked to join Tony as an equal partner, but his efforts to secure such a deal were unsuccessful.

A combination of these events resulted in an inevitable and irrevocable break from Safaris Unlimited. Tristan wanted to discuss the split over a civilised dinner, but Tony, unhappy at the prospect of losing out on future bookings, declined his invitation. He remained upset for some time

---

19 Now the Mara North Conservancy.

afterwards, but recognised the futility of feuding within such a tight-knit community and later put the acrimony of their parting behind him. Friendships were ultimately renewed, and each man was able to help the other one out in times of trouble.

The prospect of having to leave The Roost after parting company with Tony galvanised the Voorspuys into taking up an offer from their friend, Petre Barclay, to show them a cottage he knew was available for rent on a property called Deloraine. It was close to his own Madrugada Ranch near Rongai, a few miles south of the equator, on a 6,500-foot-high western elevation of the Rift Valley. Petre was a close friend of Deloraine's owner, Pam Scott, and a director of her farming company, Deloraine Ltd.

Deloraine had been home to Pam since early childhood, when her parents, Lord Francis Scott and his wife Eileen, a daughter of the Earl of Minto, a viceroy of India, had emigrated from Scotland and purchased some 3,500 acres of untamed bush in 1920 for just over £3 an acre. Over the next two years, Indian workers built an imposing family home on a site surrounded by mature trees, with sweeping views across the Rift Valley towards Nakuru. The two-storey house was constructed from large blocks of rose-tinted stone, set off by a Mangalore tiled roof, with verandas on both ground and upper floors. A huge stone fireplace dominates the central drawing room, which is a replica of one at Minto House in the Scottish borders, the ancestral home of her mother's Elliott family.

Pam's father, who was the youngest son of the sixth Duke of Buccleuch, one of the biggest landowners in Scotland, named their new home Deloraine, after the knight in Sir Walter Scott's poem, *The Lay of the Last Minstrel*. The house welcomed many distinguished visitors during the Scotts' occupation, including the Duke and Duchess of York (later King George VI and Queen Elizabeth) in 1924. Pam's niece, Alice Scott, was also a regular guest at Deloraine and returned for a two-night stay with her husband in 1936, after she had married Prince Henry, Duke of Gloucester.

Following an English education and a season in London coming out as a debutante, Pam returned to live at Deloraine when she was eighteen years old, and was put in charge of what had become a loss-making farming enterprise. Pam never married, but over the next forty years devoted her energies to developing Deloraine as a top farm in the region, installing water and fencing and building up herds of both Ayrshire and native-breed cattle. She survived the fifties Mau Mau[20] uprising unscathed, and firmly stood her ground during the uncertainty surrounding independence in 1963, when some expats packed up and went home.

By the time she reached sixty, Pam was finding the responsibilities and ties of running the enterprise increasingly onerous, and in 1979 sold out to the Rift Valley Institute of Science and Technology (RVIST). During her working life, she had expanded the farm to more than 5,000 acres, increased the cattle to 1,700 head, erected eighty-four kilometres of fencing and built more than twenty kilometres of farm roads. Pam agreed to the sale with one crucial proviso: that she retained the right to live on at Deloraine for the rest of her life, surrounded by sixty acres of her own pasture.

At the time of the Voorspuys' visit in 1990, Pam was at Nanyuki Cottage Hospital, recovering from a stroke she had suffered following a hip operation. Tristan had first met Pam on holiday in Lamu nine years earlier and remained in contact thanks to his friendship with two of her godchildren, Elizabeth Ryrie and Brian Macoun, whose maternal grandparents had emigrated to Kenya shortly before the Scotts, and established a farm at Fintry next door to Deloraine. Despite the close connections, Tristan had never visited either property and did not know what to expect when Petre swung his pick-up truck off the main Nairobi to Uganda highway, just north of Rongai, and trundled over a bridge spanning the brown Molo River.

The tarmac stops abruptly beyond the bridge and is replaced by a dirt road, pitted with deep ruts and strips of grass flourishing in-between. The track passes the simple whitewashed buildings of the Leldet Primary School, which was founded by the Scotts in the 1930s, before coming to a fork a mile further on. Here the right-hand path leads to farm buildings, while the other climbs slowly uphill to curl around a large dam, before straightening out for the final pull up to the big house.

---

20 The Mau Mau Uprising (1952–64) was a war in the British Kenya colony dominated by the Kikuyu people, who fought against the white European colonist-settlers in Kenya, the British Army, and the local Kenya Regiment.

As the vehicle bumped and jolted through a parkland vista of fenced pasture and leafy trees, the visitors would have seen green wooded hills in the distance, then paddocks giving way to colourful shrubs and sweeping lawns, rising gently to a large mansion glowing softly in the morning sun. Two gardeners retained to keep fecund lawns in check stopped working, leant on their rakes, and stared at the approaching vehicle, for visitors to Deloraine had become rare in recent months.

The Voorspuys were shown a small cottage around the back of the main house that was available for rent, took one look and agreed that a move into the single-storey building, tucked away like staff quarters, would represent downsizing at a time of their lives when they sought the opposite. 'Let's take a peek at the big house,' Tristan suggested, leading the way up wide stone steps to a veranda protected from the hot sun by seven broad stone arches.

The décor inside was a snapshot of the mid-seventies a decade and a half earlier, the walls painted various shades of yellow, according to how many coats had been applied. But the rooms were spacious with tall ceilings, and gleaming wooden floors made from cedar trees felled on the farm. The house was furnished with memorabilia and ancestral prints from the Buccleuch and Minto family estates, including a grand piano gathering dust in the corner of the huge drawing room, and a large romantic portrait of Lady Frances Scott by Philip de László hanging above the cavernous fireplace.

Upstairs they discovered chicken wire stretched across a beautiful veranda to deter bats, but the view through the mesh was of a patchwork green plain, shimmering gently in the heat and stretching for miles into the distance. Cindy remembers the six-bedroom house felt 'unloved and wanted life breathing into it.' If Deloraine had only been available, it would have made a perfect family home and an ideal base for their developing safari business.

* CHAPTER EIGHT *

Building a Life in Kenya

THE VOORSPUYS were still living at The Roost when their son Archie was born on 23rd July 1992 in Nairobi Hospital, after Cindy was induced so that Tristan could attend the birth between hectic safari commitments. Overjoyed by the latest addition to his family, the new father whisked his mother-in-law away for a late lunch at the Muthaiga Club, returning twenty-four hours later for a celebration with his male friends, at which they polished off several bottles of champagne. The following day, Tristan kissed his wife and newborn son goodbye, collected a group of clients from the Norfolk Hotel, and drove to Narok to begin a ten-day Mara riding safari.

Later that year, Cindy signalled her own determination to continue leading a full life by taking three-month-old Archie to India, where she had been selected to represent Kenya in a ten-day polo-playing tournament. Tristan had planned to travel with them, but had to pull out when approached to do a third film shoot on the beach at Malindi for *The Young Indiana Jones Chronicles*. The key scene required horses to jump a trench dug in the sand, while sticks of dynamite exploded all around them, but as Tristan reports in his diary, everything went according to plan: 'Ditch jumping goes really well even with bangs. 8 horses over perfectly.'

Cindy arrived back from India halfway through filming and immediately drove down to join her husband on the coast, where they enjoyed deep-sea fishing and swimming their horses in the sea on days off, but after a fortnight of repetitive filming, Tristan was happy to leave the Indian Ocean behind.

Tristan may have been ready for a resumption of safari life after two weeks' absence, but he and Cindy would return to the Indian Ocean with friends and family numerous times in the years ahead, usually to one of several idyllic retreats along the northern coastline between Watamu and the Somalian border, where the pristine beaches are wonderfully wild and remote. Some of their friends owned property at the coast, none more beautiful than the Barclays' simple retreat on Kiwayu Island, where enough wild oysters to make a banquet can be plucked from rocks at low tide during a ten-minute stroll, and fishermen on the mainland sell delicious mangrove crabs and exotic fresh fish.

Places like this were the perfect antidote to the fast-paced safari life; the hot and heavy tropical air induces slumber and relaxation, and is quite unlike the crisp, clean air of high-altitude destinations up country. Tristan enjoyed fishing, swimming and snorkelling, which he consistently describes as goggling in his diaries, and after he had gained his pilot's licence in 1985, tropical beaches were even easier to access.

With the absorbing excitements of safaris, Archie's arrival, and Cindy's Indian trip, thoughts of Deloraine were rather put to one side during the course of 1991, but after Pam died there in February 1992, Tristan reopened enquiries about the house's future. Petre Barclay was happy to act as a mediator between Offbeat Safaris and the RVIST owners. Through farming connections, he knew the Kenyan president, Daniel arap Moi, who was a key figure in the establishment of the Trust, and had often met him on an informal basis at his house at Kabarak. The Voorspuys took on the upkeep of Deloraine in April 1992, but decided not to move in until negotiations had been completed, although they retained a skeleton staff on full pay, and visited from Nairobi whenever time permitted.

In December 1992, the Voorspuys were thrilled to be granted permission by the trustees of the RVIST to move into Deloraine. They threw a farewell lunch party at The Roost for forty close friends, and spent the following days packing up and transporting their possessions to Deloraine, which was an eight-hour round trip by road. A week later, they left for the Mara to begin a Christmas safari, after which Cindy returned to Deloraine and set about unpacking, and exploring the many forest tracks that weave through Londiani Mountain. Tristan stayed on in the Mara to welcome an Equitours group from the USA, which was followed by a succession of back-to-back safaris that kept him away from Deloraine until the third week of February. Home at last, he fell asleep that night listening to the reassuring thump, thump, thump, of the diesel-powered generator, an evocative sound he had craved ever since childhood visits to the remote Estancia La Colina in Argentina.

Over the next three decades, the Voorspuys were to transform Deloraine into a much-loved family home and a favourite destination for an upmarket clientele. Many years later, Pam's nephew, Xan Smiley, thanked them for saving his aunt's historic home in the Rift Valley. 'Deloraine could easily have been left empty to decline and crumble after our aunt died,' he told guests at Tristan's memorial service in 2017, 'but Tristan and Cindy courageously took on the house, along with a hundred or so acres, where they could keep their horses, dogs and, later, a few cows.'

Xan praised the many improvements made to the house and grounds and ended by offering his gratitude. 'Above all, I want to thank Tristan from the bottom of my heart for preserving the spirit of the place,' he said. 'It could have died, but thanks to his warmth, his flair, his generosity, his vision and his courage, it didn't just survive. It really did take off into a tremendous second life.'

Deloraine quickly became an ideal headquarters for Offbeat Safaris and an impressive venue for entertaining clients. In the shape of things to come, Archie's christening seven months after moving in was an opportunity to throw a lunch party for thirty guests; twenty-five of them stayed overnight in the house, cottage, and tents put up on the lawn. Four stone stables behind the house were supplemented by a range of wooden ones, and the adaptation of a redundant piggery and dairy increased the equine accommodation to forty-seven stables.

Cindy assumed charge of schooling the horses up to a high standard, educating them in all disciplines so they became adept at polo, hunting and safaris. Whenever time permitted, Tristan and Cindy played polo with friends at nearby Gilgil, and also at Timau in Laikipia. As Ginger Bell's foxhounds were kennelled close to Deloraine at Lowling Farm, Tristan started to hunt regularly with them, too. According to his diary there was room for improvement, for the hounds often rioted on wild game instead of following the artificial scent that was laid over a line of inviting thorn hedges.

Tristan amended Offbeat riding safari itineraries to include a two-night stay at Deloraine as an antidote to the thrills and spills of a Mara safari, and relied on Cindy to entertain guests. Newly refurbished, the house provided a comfortable home from home, although the smoke-stained drawing-room ceiling was considered an artefact worth preserving and escaped the decorator's brush. At Deloraine guests could read, relax and wander about the magnificent gardens, but there was also a busy agenda for those who wanted to do more than soak up the ambience, including an early morning ride exploring Londiani Mountain behind the house.

The trails here weave uphill through indigenous cedar, olive and podo forest to a 9,800-foot-high bamboo-covered crater, where a guest in Pam's time once shot a rare bongo. The secretive species of antelope had vanished forever by the time the Voorspuys moved into Deloraine, along with rhino that once visited a salt lick Cindy discovered hidden amongst the undergrowth. A stay at Deloraine usually included a full day at Lake Nakuru National Park for a nearly guaranteed sighting of pink flamingos and rhino, although the reserve is fenced-in and miniscule compared to the wild majesty of the Masai Mara.

Offbeat Safaris flourished from its new headquarters, but there were always problems on safari to frustrate a life in paradise. During Tristan's eight weeks away at the beginning of 1993, robbers stole 18,000 Kenya shillings[21] from inside his tent, which he suspected was an inside job. When enquiries amongst the Maasai staff yielded no joy, he resolved to call in the local Laibon, whose advice the Maasai and Samburu tribespeople seek in time of misfortune. Laiboni – often referred to as witch doctors – are the ritual and spiritual leaders of tribal society, whose authority is based on mystical medicinal healing powers, and a divine ability to foresee the future. The Laibon is a revered figure of absolute authority, capable of commanding blind obedience from lesser mortals, as recalled by second-generation Laikipia rancher, Gilfrid Powys, whose young cousin was

21 Around £125 in today's money.

murdered on his Suyian Ranch back in 1931.

On the day in question, five Samburu warriors had been sent by a Laibon called Ngaldaiya Leaduma to procure a human head and testicles for his witchcraft, but they returned empty-handed from a raid on Meru. On their way home, the young warriors came across Dicky Powys searching for a lambing camp alone on his horse. Dicky knew and recognised the Samburu men, so he dismounted, tucked the reins behind the stirrups and walked over to speak with them. He was never seen alive again. The alarm was raised after his riderless horse returned to the stables, and in due course his partially eaten but headless remains were discovered scattered about the plains.

A hastily convened enquiry concluded that the shepherd had fallen off his horse and been eaten by lion, but that did not explain the carefully placed reins, or satisfy the local white farming community. The investigation was only reopened after the Samburu were reported to be singing 'ask the vultures who killed the white man' at a tribal party. Ngaldaiya Leaduma was convicted at the subsequent re-trial, and Dicky's skull was returned so that it could join the rest of his remains in a shallow grave at Suyian. The Laibon was deported to the Seychelles, but the real killers were never brought to justice.

Sixty intervening years and huge cultural and political change within Kenya had not diminished the Laibon's power or standing in the community, although the medicine man invited into the Offbeat camp by Tristan was a force for good, not evil. He arrived draped in animal skins, carrying a huge bone, and addressed the small group of staff assembled in front of him, demanding that the thief amongst them confess to his crime. When no one came forward, he positioned the bone carefully on the ground and asked each person to walk over it slowly, predicting that the culprit would be dead within weeks. Three weeks later, the man Tristan suspected of committing the crime contracted malaria and died.

Other safari adventures during Offbeat's early years often teetered on a knife edge between triumph and disaster. This was never more apparent than during crossings of the Mara River, which was a highlight of every Offbeat Mara riding safari and an experience guests looked forward to and dreaded in equal measure. The Mara River begins life as a myriad of streams draining the Mau Escarpment before flowing past the Loita Hills, where most of Tristan's early Mara rides began, and continuing through the grasslands of what is now the Mara North Conservancy.

From there the river meanders on into the Masai Mara National Reserve, where it lies in the direct path of migrating wildebeest and other plains game, which must cross to the west bank in order to continue their perpetual quest for fresh grazing on the Serengeti plains. Natural history films portraying this hazardous stage of the migration concentrate on huge Nile crocodiles making the most of a bounteous feast that lasts from July until September.

Crocodiles and hippo also thrive upstream, where the winding watercourse cuts a steep brown trench through the Mara North savannah. Riders on an Offbeat safari must cross the river hereabouts to continue their journey to the summit of the Siria Escarpment, where they can admire far-reaching views to the Serengeti in Tanzania, and congratulate themselves on having survived thus far. Crossings were relatively straightforward when the river was running at its normal height and the horses' feet stayed put on the muddy bottom, but were much more hazardous when they had to swim for it following heavy rains. Many riders arrived at the river expecting clear water and were perturbed to find a dark, coffee-coloured flow, through which underwater predators could sneak up undetected.

Trails along this stretch of the river drop down steeply to shallow rapids, where animals can reach the far bank without disturbing large pods of hippopotami wallowing in deeper water downstream. Male hippo are territorial and aggressive, but all adults sport huge incisors and canines that never stop growing. These teeth self-sharpen as they grind together and are dangerously effective in combat, capable of tearing lumps of flesh from a rival's body, or chomping a canoe clean in half. None of Tristan's horses had yet been attacked by a hippo, but a collision with one in the water would be unlikely to have a happy ending.

Crocodiles are much less conspicuous but also prefer deeper water, which is why Tristan permitted his clients to swim in faster stretches of the Mara River, although huge reptiles slithering into the water at their approach dissuaded most from even trying. The aggressive Nile crocodile is an opportunistic and solitary predator, prepared to wait motionless for days on end for a meal to come within range of lightning-quick teeth, and powerful jaws that clamp the victim in a vice-like grip. The crocodile then drowns its hapless prey, before stashing the corpse in an underwater larder to be devoured at leisure. There are records of large adults successfully killing giraffe, Cape buffalo and even a black rhinoceros, but despite their fearsome reputation, Tristan had never lost a horse to one.

Thoughts of crocodile and hippo were likely to have been on everyone's mind as they approached the Mara River in September 1993, for her waters were churning angrily in spate, albeit at a level Tristan felt confident was fordable. The group had been assembled by Count Konrad Goess-Saurau, and included his wife Susie, and his twenty-two-year-old nephew, Xandi Maculan, who had recently left the Austrian Army. They had enjoyed a brilliant safari so far, galloping with giraffe, being charged by an elephant, jumping in and out of Maasai bomas,[22] and savouring the confidence and camaraderie that accompanies a white-knuckle adventure. When they reached the river, Tristan rode up and down the bank before deciding on a suitable crossing place, scrambled down to the water's edge, and urged his horse into the torrent. Everyone could see the wet grey backs of several hippo downstream and hear them grunting noisily above the bustling flow.

'There was not the slightest doubt that the horses would have to swim for it,' Xandi remembers thinking, as he contemplated his fate overlooking the rolling brown waters. Susie went next, but her horse was turned upside down by an unseen obstruction when halfway across, emerging a few seconds later with its sodden rider still in the saddle having survived an Eskimo roll. Tristan reached the far bank in time to see Xandi's horse, Nightcap, hit the same obstacle and momentarily vanish beneath the water. Nightcap resurfaced with his rider hanging onto the neck strap, but when the horse gave up the struggle and began to drift lifelessly downstream, Xandi let him go and struck out for shore.

At this moment Tristan leapt, fully clothed, into the dirty brown water and swam fifty yards out to the stricken horse, which had drifted into a

---

22 A small livestock enclosure or stockade, normally constructed from thorny branches to deter predators.

deeper and infinitely more dangerous section of the river. Tristan grabbed the reins and whilst treading water, held Nightcap's head above the flow to revive his flagging spirits, before striking out for shore with the reins still in his hands.

When they reached the bank nearly a hundred yards downstream, the only foothold was a narrow, submerged ledge, where Nightcap lay blowing heavily on his side as Tristan released the saddle girth and kept a wary eye on hippos wallowing thirty yards from where they had come to rest. The horse eventually staggered up on shaky limbs to join his rescuer standing in a foot of water, but they were trapped at the base of an eight-foot-high cliff. An assistant galloped back to camp and returned an hour later with men and spades to excavate a tunnel, so that Nightcap could be freed before dark.

The gelding made a full recovery, but what Xandi remembers most is Tristan's determination to save the horse regardless of the risks involved. 'Tristan had no regard for his own safety,' he recalled twenty-five years later, 'none whatsoever.' That evening Tristan opened his diary to make a note of the day's events. 'Move to Mara River,' he wrote in blue biro. 'Charged by elephant. Much drama with Nightcap in river.'

✦ CHAPTER NINE ✦

Stories from the Sky

PROVIDED he was not committed to a safari of his own, Tristan could never resist an invitation to explore a new piece of Africa, and in June 1991 he joined Roland Purcell for a trip down to Mahale Mountains on the shores of Lake Tanganyika in Tanzania. Roland had moved to Africa to work for a Nairobi auction house after a stint with Sotheby's in the UK, and had been an itinerant lodger at The Roost with the Voorspuys, before ending up at a remote tourist camp in Mahale Mountains National Park, where forest-living chimpanzees were the star attraction. He and Tristan shared many similarities, for both had left their homelands to seek adventure in Africa, were fascinated by nature, and were drawn to faraway wild places.

Roland flew Tristan down to Mahale Mountains in his plane after the end of a Mara safari, soaring above a parched brown landscape, which after five-hours flying gave way to a mountainous terrain of tall peaks and plunging verdant slopes. The pilot swung his Cessna 206 expertly down the valleys, so the summits towered steeply above them and the sides rushed past in a swirling green blur, before skimming low over Lake Tanganyika, shimmering sapphire blue in the afternoon heat.

After Roland had landed on the tiny lakeside airstrip, they were taken up to the camp by boat, where Tristan found the white sand too hot for comfort and hurriedly slipped on his deck shoes. Later that evening, he sat outside the tall thatched dining-room with a cold beer and watched the faint, far-off outline of the Congo fade from sight across the lake. This was a place Tristan had heard so much about and had wanted to visit more than any other. Before retiring to bed, he wrote in his diary, 'Mahale at last.'

During the three-day visit, Tristan saw a chimp grooming his male companion, sifting through the hair as a human mother might scour her child's head for nits, and watched others prise ants from a tree trunk with sticks. Chimpanzees' abilities to improvise tools in this way had been discovered by the British anthropologist, Jane Goodall, at nearby Gombe Stream National Park two decades earlier. Her acclaimed research also found that chimps were capable of rational thought and clear displays of affection, such as those witnessed by Tristan during his stay.

He was captivated by the primates' noisy and excited displays of pant hooting,[23] but saw none of the darker behaviour that Goodall also uncovered during her research. Eleven years after Tristan first visited Greystoke Camp, a male chimpanzee from the Gombe colony immortalised by Goodall's book, *In the Shadow of Mankind,* snatched a fourteen-month-old baby from the back of an African woman and carried the screaming infant high into the treetops to eat it, leaving the remains straddling the branch of a tree.

Tristan also spotted red colobus and red-tailed monkeys, caught colourful fish, and enjoyed sailing on board *Zoe*, a wooden dhow built at the small village of Ujiji on the shores of Lake Tanganyika, better known as the place where the British explorers, Stanley and Dr Livingstone, met up in November 1871. By the time he left, Mahale Mountains and Greystoke Camp had made a lasting impression.

The flight there had also inspired Tristan to make a start on his next challenge, which when completed, would add another dimension to his abilities and growing reputation as a top safari guide. He knew that remote and beautiful places such as Mahale Mountains were not accessible by road, and that some of the most exciting destinations in Africa could only be reached by light aircraft. Many of his Kenyan friends owned planes, and used them like cars to skip between parties, polo and work, in a way that was synonymous with the East African lifestyle he so enjoyed. Ten days after returning from his chimpanzee safari, Tristan took his first flying lesson, but he waited three more years before buying a plane of his own.

Early in 1994, Tristan heard that an English friend had flown a

---

23 One of the best known vocalisations of chimpanzees. The call begins with breathy, low-pitched hoots that make a transition into a series of quicker, higher-pitched, in-and-out pants.

Cessna 206 home from Canada and, with a sale agreed in principle, he flew over England to conclude the deal. In selecting a Cessna 206, he had chosen a true plane of the African bush, widely respected for its powerful engine, rugged construction and spacious cabin. The American manufacturers describe the single-engine aircraft with fixed landing gear as the sport-utility vehicle of the air, and claim suitability for a wide variety of uses.

The gleaming white machine that awaited Tristan at Turweston Airfield in Buckinghamshire had the registration N3998Q superimposed in white letters onto a dark go-faster stripe running the full length of the fuselage, set off by a handsome, three-blade black propeller on the nose. The seller recommended removing the aircraft's wings and shipping it across to Africa by container, but Tristan was determined to fly his new purchase home. The only problem with his ambitious plan was that he had not yet qualified as a pilot.

But he knew a man who had. Not one to pass up the chance of adventure, Roland Purcell agreed to fly the plane back to Kenya, with Tristan as the co-pilot beside him. In the meantime, N3998Q had been equipped with a ferry tank to carry fuel for an extra seven hours in the air, although Roland pointed out that an additional 500 litres of inflammable liquid also transformed the plane into a flying bomb.

He was surprised when Tristan produced a map of the Roman Empire in the belief that it would be fit for purpose, since it covered the entire journey from Turweston in England to Nairobi in Kenya. The friends decided they would fly whenever possible at around 8,000 feet under Visual Flight Rules (VFR), the regulations under which a pilot operates when conditions are sufficiently clear to see land, and, as N3998Q was not equipped with radar, they agreed not to fly in the dark.

Tristan, Cindy, Archie and Roland all stayed with Sorrel and her family in Northamptonshire the night before the great journey got underway at Turweston on a balmy May morning. The airfield had opened in 1942 as an RAF Bomber Command training base, which Henk Voorspuy would almost certainly have visited during the Second World War, but such thoughts were far from everyone's mind as they sipped a farewell glass of champagne in warm sunshine. Wearing smart crew uniforms, the pilots squeezed into seats behind the dashboard, pulled on their headphones and began preparing the instruments for take-off.

Most of the space behind them was taken up by the ferry tank and an inflatable paddling pool that Cindy had insisted Tristan bring home for Archie, pointing out that it could come in useful as a raft in the event of an accident. Ten minutes later, N3998Q trundled down the grass airstrip, before lifting steeply into blue skies and banking round in a farewell fly-by for the tiny figures waving far below. 'We were shockingly underprepared, but full of confidence,' Roland admitted, when recalling the start of the flight twenty-three years later.

Forty minutes after taking off from Turweston, they touched down in Southampton to clear customs, before flying on to Cannes in the South of France, where a hotel had been booked for the night. They had their first scare the next day, when fuel ran back into the ferry tank and gave the aeroplane 'a cough' over Corsica, which was only resolved when Tristan telephoned the mechanic in Turweston for advice.

The Tyrrhenian Sea glittered a brilliant blue as they flew between Elba and Montecristo to pick up the Italian coast a hundred miles south of Rome and then skim low above the ragged Apennine Mountains, following the high spine of Italy through glorious clear skies, before heading east above the heel to land in Corfu for a two-night stay.

Tristan had an altercation with a stall holder in Corfu Town that evening, after he had knocked down five out of six tin soldiers at a fairground shooting range. When the sixth remained upright despite being hit in exactly the same place as the others, Tristan suspected foul play and demanded a large pink gorilla as his legitimate prize. Fuelled by a sense of righteous indignation, he objected so vigorously that the proprietor eventually handed the toy over.

There was little space for additional baggage on board the already cramped plane, but the issue had become such a matter of principle that the pink gorilla was crammed in as another present for Archie back home. Perhaps the fairground experience explained Tristan's condemnation of Corfu in a letter to Sorrel as having been 'spoilt by British package tourists', although he enjoyed exploring hills covered in beautiful spring flowers the following day.

The flight to Luxor above the Mediterranean started well, but after entering Egyptian airspace it became clear their traffic controllers were much more officious than their European counterparts, and the plane was soon being re-routed on minor but irritating detours. One hundred and eighty miles from Luxor, these inconveniences were supplanted by something much more menacing, when Roland spotted a distant yellow wall ahead. The mood inside the cabin darkened with the realisation they were flying straight into the teeth of a desert haboob; Tristan remembered the vicious storm in Khartoum twelve years earlier, but Roland had never experienced the extreme conditions that were about to test his pilot's instincts and abilities to the full.

Moments later a savage sandstorm overcame them, instantly reducing visibility to less than a hundred yards as Roland searched for a way out of the yellow haze. 'We were in the unknown and I didn't have great confidence in the outcome,' he remembers. 'Stan was very calm and told me that it's my call – he was the best possible guy you could hope to have in the seat beside you in a situation like that.' Egyptian flight control had taken them away from the Nile Valley in the interests of security, but poor visibility and the danger of engine failure through sand blockage forced Roland to drop altitude and head east to Asyut on the Blue Nile, where the GPS informed them an airstrip awaited. 'The amazing GPS has all the answers,' Tristan enthused in his letter, 'it tells us exactly where we are, and the distance to where we want to go. Quite reassuring as we groped our way through the gloom.'

The GPS put N3998Q slap on the runway at Asyut, where they sat in the half-light for two hours trying in vain to communicate with a seemingly deserted control tower. It was only when two armed soldiers appeared out of the murk that Roland and Tristan realised they had landed, without permission, on a military airstrip where goats scavenging weeds on the runway added to a surreal sense of isolation. It was late afternoon by the time military personnel had finished interrogating the bewildered Englishmen and allowed them to depart on the sixty-minute flight to Luxor, but after they were airborne, flight control at Cairo warned them it would soon be too dark to fly by VFR.

Roland's response to being ordered back to land was to confirm they would fly by IFR (Instrument Flight Rules) instead, even though he was not qualified to do so. Cairo responded by insisting they climb to 10,000 feet, an altitude that would stretch the little Cessna with so much fuel on board. Roland flew as high as he dared, but Tristan realised the plane had made a complete U-turn during the confusion of simultaneously trying to read instruments, gain altitude and navigate through the dark. 'Luckily I had learnt a bit by this stage,' he told Sorrel, 'so was able to do my bit as a co-pilot and tell Roland to turn around. It was not much fun, as you could see no lights below and precious few stars, so we became rather lonely.'

An hour later they landed at Luxor, exhausted by the strain of the last eighteen hours, but grateful to have survived a series of potential disasters. The relief expressed in Tristan's letter to Sorrel is tangible: 'Boy were we grateful to land on a huge 24-hour runway with all the lights.' The next morning, he awoke refreshed from a good night's sleep, but when exploring the hot streets of Luxor, again took exception to the way animals were treated by the locals. In a crowded market place, he came across an Egyptian repeatedly thrashing a worn-out, starving horse, as it tried to pull an overloaded cart through the maze of colourful stalls. As bemused locals looked on in astonishment, Roland intervened to prevent his friend from meting out similar punishment to the stallion's heartless owner.

The travellers planned to overfly Sudan on the penultimate leg of their journey to Lodwar in northern Kenya, but when they left Luxor after a twenty-four-hour stay, their flight plan had still not been approved by the Sudanese authorities. They had been given clearance for an alternative and much longer route overflying Ethiopia via Djibouti, but as he explained to his sister, Tristan was determined to take the shorter option: 'We decided to try and run for it by keeping quiet once we had left Egypt and hoped the Gypos did not pass us on to Khartoum.' The flight was closely monitored as far as the Sudanese border at Abu Simbel on the west shore of Lake Nasser, where it was something of a relief to leave Egypt behind. 'Finally Abu Simbel and goodbye N3998Q,' Tristan wrote. 'We change course to avoid Khartoum and fly a thousand miles without anyone knowing.'

Sudanese air control did not respond when Roland tried to contact them, which he took as encouragement to continue flying south above the shimmering yellow desert for another six hours. 'As soon as you land in a foreign country, you are completely at their mercy,' Roland explained later, 'but it's a different story up in the air. We just turned the radio off and kept flying – the Sudanese weren't going to scramble jets to intercept a Cessna 206.'

Danger closer to the ground was another matter, for a civil war had been raging between north and south Sudan since 1983, and Tristan was not prepared to risk his new plane by flying within range of rebel missiles. Flying as high as the regular non-turbo engine would permit, the pilots could still make out isolated bomas strewn like brown pebbles about the sandy landscape beneath them, and discern faint, ghost-like tracks that ran out of life in the middle of nowhere.

As they approached the upper reaches of the White Nile, where Ethiopia juts out into southern Sudan, the desert ran away to greener plains and brown streams rushing beneath blue storm clouds bulging on the horizon. When the first spits of rain started to rattle the wiperless windscreen, Roland assumed control of the plane before they were enveloped by a savage storm that blurred vision and drove needles of cold water into the cockpit. A severe thunderstorm is capable of sucking a light aircraft thousands of feet into a vortex of turbulence, before spitting it out at an altitude where even the most experienced pilot has no chance of maintaining visual reference to the ground. When the wing load in these conditions is exceeded, the plane enters a graveyard spiral and disintegrates into several pieces. For this reason, the US Federal Aviation Administration recommends that light aircraft do not approach within twenty nautical miles of a severe thunderstorm.

If the Cessna had been equipped with weather radar, Roland would have been able to avoid the most dangerous, pulsing eye of the storm, but his only hope in these circumstances was to identify a gap in the nimbus and fly through it to calmer and safer skies below. He did not hesitate when a rip appeared in the clouds beneath him, but dropped the plane's nose and shoved the throttle forward to plummet five thousand feet in less than ninety seconds, while Tristan struggled to prevent paraphernalia shored up behind them from smashing onto the dashboard. Tristan's account provides chilling insight into the terrifying ordeal: 'No visibility and starting to get bumpy, we had fifteen minutes of this with white knuckles showing and not a friend for 200 miles. We see a gap and Roland dives from 9,500 to 4,800 feet in about one and a half minutes.'

Miraculously, N3998Q emerged safely beneath the storm, but directly above a rebel bush camp and airstrip in Pochalla County, on the Sudan border with Ethiopia. A few anxious moments followed, during which the pilots wondered what armed militia staring skywards must be thinking about a light aircraft dive-bombing their camp, and wished the plane could travel faster than its top speed of 120 knots. 'Another long moment passes' before they are out of danger, and notice that the land below is now neither desert yellow nor lush green, but a harsh, overgrazed ochre.

As the Kenyan outpost of Lodwar loomed into view, so did the bottle-green patina of the Jade Sea to the east, and the distant peaks of Mounts Kulal and Nyiru glowing in sharp relief beneath the setting sun. Eleven hours and fifty minutes after leaving Luxor, both men clambered out of the plane at Lodwar on unsteady feet, to be greeted by a crowd of smiling children. There was a shower, loo and running water at Turkwel Lodge in town, but as Tristan wrote in his letter, 'We could have slept anywhere.'

Next morning, they flew out over Lake Turkana and on to Nakuru, where they surreptitiously landed at Petre Barclay's Madrugada airstrip to meet Cindy, offload baggage and change into clean crew uniforms for customs and immigration in Nairobi, where they were waved through carrying two bottles of chilled champagne presented by Cindy an hour earlier. The friends had spent thirty-six hours sitting next to each other in the tiny plane, during which, Tristan proudly revealed to his sister, neither man had resorted to using the empty Lucozade bottle that served as an emergency urinal. He ended his long and detailed description of the hair-raising journey with an apology. 'Well, there is a boring account of the flight,' he wrote. 'Sorry to get carried away. All I have to do now is deregister the plane and learn to fly.'

If Tristan had left Turweston with six of his nine lives intact, there is no question that he arrived in Nairobi having expended at least one more during a journey that Roland describes as one of the last great flying adventures. Within six months, Tristan had gained his private pilot's licence and changed his plane's registration to the Kenyan prefix of 5Y followed by his own initials of TMV. A month after qualifying as a pilot, but with only two hours' solo flying under his belt, Tristan flew the family down to Malindi for a holiday beside the Indian Ocean. They were joined by friends, including the former equestrian world champion Lucinda Green, but the most treasured guest of all was the Voorspuys' new four-month-old daughter. Imogen (Imo) had been born in the same Nairobi hospital as her brother on 20th August 1994, and her arrival completed the Voorspuy family unit.

Tristan and Roland's remarkable international flight was only the first of a series of accidents, mishaps and near-misses that characterised Tristan's flying career. A year after her international flight, 5Y TMV's tail was bent like a banana when she rolled into an acacia tree, after Tristan forgot to put chocks behind the wheels having landed at Crescent Island on Lake Naivasha, ruining his plans to fly down to Zimbabwe for a polo tour. 'Woke up to find TMV has run into a tree,' Tristan lamented in his diary. 'DISASTER. I have forgotten chocks. Dreadful day.' Luckily, a friend and fellow polo player called Philip McLellan, universally known as Flip Flop, offered to fly him down to Harare in his own plane instead.

Flying home over the remote Ruaha National Park in Tanzania at an altitude of 9,500 feet, the engine on Flip Flop's Cessna 180 coughed briefly, then shut down altogether with a fuel blockage, above a vast wilderness panorama of savannah and thorny scrub. Flip Flop assumed control and sent out a mayday call with their position to indicate a life-threatening emergency, which was picked up by flight control at Dar es Salaam. But when he handed over the GPS for Tristan to continue broadcasting their position, the device shut down, and with it any hope of an accurate search-and-rescue operation.

The Cessna glided serenely lower in eerie silence as Flip Flop prepared to crash land on a strip of level grassland beside a small stream, but the engine suddenly spluttered and then roared back to life as fuel made it through the lines to the carburettor, when only five hundred feet above ground on the final approach. The plane levelled out above flat-topped acacia trees, before climbing slowly back into the safety of blue skies. 'Fuel stoppage and mayday over Ruaha,' Tristan noted in his diary on 29th June

1995, 'very exciting.' He might have added *another life down*.

Within twelve months of the Ruaha incident, Tristan was once more in trouble in the skies, running into thick cloud and turbulence above the Usambara Mountains in Tanzania, following a trip to see his friend Bimb Theobald. As clouds closed in, Tristan decided to fly through the cloying white fog to clearer skies above, but Johnny Camm in the seat beside him was convinced the safest option was to lose height and keep within sight of the ground. Cindy and her fellow passenger, Chris Wilson, could only watch in horror as the altercation between the two pilots grew increasingly heated, while the plane rose and fell like a porpoise through the white-out.

Knowing they were surrounded by tall mountains, Chris spoke for everyone when he muttered between the bumps, 'We are all going to die.' His chilling prediction may have persuaded Tristan to relent after much conflict and confusion in the cockpit, and accept Johnny's advice to drop down below cloud level, where they regained visibility. Tristan later gave Johnny a painting commemorating the ordeal; the cartoon-style picture depicts his friend wearing dark glasses astride his favourite polo pony, with a cigarette dangling from his lips and a pint of beer balanced precariously on his pony's backside. In the background, the artist has sketched a stricken light aircraft with 5Y TMV inscribed on the wings, and legs and arms protruding from the cockpit.

On 29th January 1997, Tristan was fortunate not to join the long list of African adventurers who have met their death in the sky, not least Karen Blixen's lover, Denys Finch Hatton, who perished at the controls of his own plane in 1931. Tristan's closest shave in a light aircraft was a consequence of his own generosity in agreeing to take on board an extra passenger, who radioed to ask for a lift as he was preparing to take off from the Barclays' Madrugada airstrip. When the request came through, Tristan had already taken Irish friends Peter and Jane Magnier and Iona McGregor on board, and was preparing to fly them up to the Kamogi Ranch[24] in Laikipia, before continuing to Nairobi after lunch. The plane turned back to collect the hitch-hiker, who was sheltering from the fierce midday sun inside a hangar. Tristan could see he was a big man and noticed him

---

24 Owned by the Voorspuys' friends, Nick and Heather Day.

sweating profusely as he carried a heavy case through the hot, breathless air.

By the time the passenger and his luggage had been taken on board, a light breeze had got up out of the north to send fragments of mown grass tumbling along the airstrip, and shake the orange windsock into flickering life. Ten minutes later, 5Y TMV was back where it started and once more ready to take off, but the warm breeze was now blowing in powerful, intermittent gusts from the north. Conversation inside the cabin fell silent, as the engine's clattering roar drowned all sound and Tristan sent his plane speeding along the runway without a second glance.

If he had looked over his right shoulder, Tristan would have seen the canvas windsock rippling at full stretch and realised he was about to take off with the wind at his tail. Onlookers watched the plane lift from the ground, saw it shudder as the fierce tail wind took hold, briefly stand *Titanic*-like on its tail, and then plummet earthwards two hundred yards beyond the end of the runway.

Clouds of thick dust were already settling when Cindy arrived at the scene in her car five minutes later, to find the plane upside down on its back in a maize field, with the passengers suspended from their seatbelts like bats. Apart from one broken finger, they were miraculously unharmed, but 5Y TMV was a write-off and never took to the skies again. The plane was replaced by a Cessna 180 with the registration 5Y AYN, which also suffered her share of knocks and blows, including minor collisions with acacia thorn trees in the Chalbi Desert. Tristan was still piloting 5Y AYN eighteen years after writing off her predecessor, but would suffer further flying mishaps and tragedies in the years ahead.

The worst of these would involve gyrocopters, a flying machine that resembles a miniature helicopter. However, unlike a helicopter, the free-spinning rotor blade is self-propelled by the upwards passage of air, and until 2010 the cockpit of all gyrocopters was exposed to the elements, which led to the moniker 'motorbikes of the skies'. The forward thrust required to initiate and maintain the spinning rotor blade is provided by a small engine-driven propeller, but in order to economise on space, the fuel for most early models was stored in a tank beneath the driver's seat. Tristan was introduced to gyrocopters by his close friend Johnny

Camm a year after writing off his aeroplane, and joined him for a flight above the bamboo-carpeted crater on top of Londiani Mountain, where he experienced the same exhilarating rush of fresh air and excitement as when galloping on horseback, or opening the throttle of a motorbike.

Tristan was so enamoured by the gyrocopter experience that he bought Johnny's machine soon afterwards and hired an instructor to teach him how to fly it. Tristan's flower-growing neighbour, Willy Potgieter, had recently gained his own pilot's wings and since Tristan was keen to involve his flying friends in all things aviation, he invited him along to watch the first lesson. Willy arrived at the airstrip on Hamish Grant's farm at Gogar in time to see Tristan squeeze into the small seat for his first solo take-off, offer a cheery wave, and open the throttle to send the tiny machine jolting down the centre of the grass runway. He watched the gyro lift momentarily above the ground, wobble precariously in the air, and then disappear in a cloud of thick dust.

Willy and the speechless instructor jumped into Tristan's Land Rover and sped off down the runway, not knowing what to expect at the other end. They found the gyrocopter wedged tight against a barbed-wire fence with the engine idling and the rotor blade stationary. The pilot was trapped inside the machine, held fast by a strand of barbed wire pressed so tightly against his neck that blood was trickling down into his shirt. 'Get me out of here,' he said in a hoarse whisper, unable to move or turn his head.

After Willy had cut him free, Tristan ripped off his helmet and exclaimed, 'What a bloody fool I am.' He had forgotten to fasten the chin strap on his helmet, which had flipped up to blind him at the crucial moment of take-off. Undeterred, Tristan got back into the machine, taxied back to the start of the runway and executed a faultless take-off with his chin strap firmly secured.

After he had completed a few lessons, Tristan felt confident enough to fly his machine back home from his neighbour's farm at Gogar. The airstrip had not yet been built at Deloraine, but Johnny Camm had landed his own gyrocopter successfully in a paddock behind the stables there, so Tristan telephoned his friend for advice. He was told not to land with the wind behind him under any circumstances, even if that meant an unnerving downhill approach.

Tristan's niece, Tam Woods, who was staying at the time, remembers her uncle planning the flight over breakfast on Easter Monday, unperturbed by the prospect of landing downhill. Tristan asked to be dropped off at Gogar, but on her return to Deloraine fifteen minutes later, Tam met Tristan hobbling painfully towards the house looking white as a sheet. 'When I asked what had happened, I only remember a bark and a grumble in reply,' she says, 'but after seeing him into the house, I snuck back out to take a look.'

Tam found the shattered gyrocopter lying on its side, after the rotor blade had struck the ground on landing and caused the machine to disintegrate into several pieces; strapped into his seat above the petrol tank, Tristan had miraculously been thrown clear of danger. Cindy was away skiing with Archie at the time, but on her return to Deloraine, staff told her they could not believe her husband had walked away from the wreckage unscathed. 'He should have been dead,' said one. Tristan did not replace his gyrocopter, and the hangar he built to house it was turned into a hay barn. His dalliance with gyrocopters had lasted barely a year, but by anyone's reckoning it had cost him at least two more of his nine lives, and by lunchtime on Easter Monday 1999, he had only one left.

CHAPTER TEN

Of Lion and Buffalo

WITH a young family, a full life at Deloraine, and back-to-back safaris during the busy dry-season months, Tristan realised during the course of 1994 that he was going to need the help of another guide to keep pace with the burgeoning demands on his time, but no one sprang immediately to mind. He appreciated the help of gap-year students, but most only stayed for a few months before returning to the UK, just when they had learnt enough to be of real help. These young men and women were referred to as gappies, and over the years several were to arrive at Deloraine after their parents had been clients on an Offbeat safari. A few ended up staying much longer and became an integral part of the operation, but genuine gappies lacked the skill or gravitas to be given positions of real responsibility.

A fully fledged riding safari guide requires a rare combination of skills that include detailed knowledge of the bush and wildlife, the ability to ride well, and the aptitude to communicate with guests and camp staff alike. Any guide working for Tristan would also need boundless energy, the hide of a rhinoceros, and the stamina to stay up around the campfire until the last client had turned in for the night.

These thoughts were far from Tristan's mind when he walked into the bar of the Manyatta Polo Club at Gilgil after chukkas[25] one Sunday afternoon and bumped into twenty-seven-year-old Mark Laurence enjoying a cold beer. The two men struck up a conversation, during which Tristan learnt that Mark was a second-generation Kenyan who had enjoyed a successful career as a jockey that began as a sixteen-year-old apprentice.

---

25 A chukka is a period of play during a game of polo, generally last 7.5 minutes. Polo practice is loosely referred to as playing chukkas.

After being crowned champion jockey in Kenya, Mark had moved to England to ride for the leading National Hunt trainer Josh Gifford, before returning to Kenya and finding work as an overland safari guide for an Italian tour operator.

Tristan grew increasingly interested as he listened to the former jockey's potted life history, his fascination for the bush and the revelation that he spoke fluent Swahili. Several whiskies later, he looked Mark up and down one more time and told him, 'Fuck guiding in Land Rovers. You can ride, come and guide for me.' A week later, Mark joined the Offbeat team and stayed for the next twelve years, during which he became known as 'Sparky', after turning up at a fancy-dress party kitted out as a lightbulb.

Remembering his own baptism of fire when starting work for Tony Church, Tristan asked Mark to be his assistant on a couple of rides, before sending him off on his own. Guests were already seated for dinner during Mark's first safari with Tristan, when a night watchman came into the Olare Lamun[26] campsite to warn that lion were bothering the horses. Game viewing opportunities with Tristan always took precedence over everything else, so dinner was temporarily abandoned as guests jumped into the Land Rover for the short journey to where the horses were tethered on a long rope. Tristan employed askari watchmen[27] to protect his horses at night, but the sentries had abandoned their posts and were huddled in the back of the nearby lorry, jabbering excitedly and banging tins together to keep the predators at bay.

Mark picked up several lion lurking with menacing intent in the beam of his spotlight, and as they retreated into the darkness, Tristan stepped out of the Land Rover wearing the colonial East African evening attire of a colourful cotton kikoy,[28] laundered shirt and blue flip flops. Mark shone the light on the retreating lion as Tristan ran through the long grass towards them, cradling a glass of whisky and repeating at the top of his

---

26 Olare Lamun means 'place of the rhino salt lick'. The name has always appeared in Offbeat Safari itineraries spelt this way, but can also be spelt Olare Lemuny.

27 Night watchmen.

28 A cotton wrap-around sarong originating from coastal communities of the Indian Ocean and is a popular casual garment worn throughout Kenya.

voice, 'Leave my bloody horses alone,' not relenting until he was convinced they had gone off to find easier prey.

During his next safari, Mark witnessed a rare case of mistaken identity, when Tristan spotted what he believed to be cheetah lying amongst thick scrub on the sides of a rocky kopje.[29] As the riders approached the cats, one of them volunteered that the cheetah looked remarkably like a lion to him, but was summarily dismissed by an indignant Tristan.

'Someone hold my horse,' he barked, after dismounting fifty yards from the kopje. 'If you lot just wait here, I will go round the back and flush them out.' Unlike lion, which weigh up to 500lbs and qualify as one of Africa's dangerous Big Five species of game, adult cheetah rarely weigh more than 130lbs and have beautiful yellow coats covered with nearly two thousand irregular black spots. With a top speed of seventy miles per hour, they are faster than any other animal on earth, but the slender diurnal hunters pose no real threat to human life.

Tristan knew there was little risk attached to flushing a cheetah from its hiding place, but within a dozen steps, several well-camouflaged lion stood up from the scrub and stared at the intruder. Tristan backed slowly away from danger, one careful step at a time, as a dozen tufted black tails twitched angrily from side to side. He turned around on reaching open ground, and walked somewhat gingerly back to the riders, who were waiting in awkward silence. Tristan threw a sheepish grin at the client who had warned him the cheetah was a lion. 'My mistake,' he admitted, 'I owe you an apology.'

Despite the risk they posed to his clients, Tristan knew lion were close to the top of most people's wish list of animals to see from the back of a horse. He valued the pride living near Olare Orok, which over the course of many years became habituated to the presence of humans and horses, but his diaries are peppered with references to mock charges and stand-offs with the big cats.

One of these encounters took place during a Mara riding safari with the American actress, Glenn Close, and her teenage daughter Annie, in March 2001. Annie and her friend were bringing up the rear of the ride, when

---

29 A rocky outcrop often covered in thick scrub.

a young lioness slipped out of the bushes and sprinted up to her horse's backside. Rory Hensman's son, Sean, who was riding immediately in front of Annie as Tristan's assistant guide, heard her terrified scream and spun his horse round to confront the lion, which stopped dead in her tracks. Sean urged his horse forwards with only a branch to defend himself and smacked the bemused lioness hard in the face, seconds before Tristan galloped up cracking a leather hunting whip loudly above his head.

That lion was not the first or last to be faced down by Tristan wielding his trusty whip, which he maintained was an infinitely better way of dealing with an aggressive big cat than a deadly bullet. He never carried a rifle on safari, and many a lion that might otherwise have been shot in the interests of client safety, ran off with the sound of whipcord ringing in its ears.

Tristan had something of a lion tamer's confidence about him when dealing with big cats, and believed it was fatal to try and run away from a charging lion, but he was well aware of their fearsome record and reputation. A pair of notorious lion in Tsavo killed dozens of workers during construction of the Kenya to Uganda railway in 1898, before being shot by Lt Col John Henry Patterson, who described his experiences in his book, *The Man-Eaters of Tsavo*. During the 1930s and 40s, a professional hunter named George Rusby destroyed an infamous pride of Tanganyikan[30] lion that during the course of three generations were thought to have killed and eaten more than 1,500 human victims.

More recently, scientists established an increase of man-eating attacks in what is now Tanzania, which resulted in more than five hundred separate incidents during a fifteen-year time frame dating from 1990. A man-eater killed by game scouts in April 2004 is believed to have devoured at least thirty-five people in a series of incidents around the Rufiji Delta region of southern Tanzania. Like one of the Tsavo lions, the culprit was found to be suffering from painful tooth decay, but a scarcity of natural prey due to human encroachment and associated loss of habitat are thought to be the real reasons for an increase in man-eating habits.

Tristan lamented the big cats' decline and rapid contraction of range

30 Tanganyika is now Tanzania.

after they became extinct from the North African countries of Djibouti, Egypt and Eritrea during the 1960s. Lion have been listed as vulnerable on the IUCN Red List since 1996, and populations outside designated protection areas in Sub-Saharan Africa have little chance of long-term survival due to ongoing conflict with humans.

This conflict is historically acute on the rolling savannah straddling Kenya and Tanzania, where the Maasai people have grazed their livestock for thousands of years and protected them from lion and other predators at night by building impenetrable thorn enclosures known as bomas. Maasai are sustained by the flesh, blood and milk of their cattle, which are also regarded as symbols of prestige and wealth, and their belief that all cattle on earth belong to them used to result in bloody raids against neighbouring tribes. Lion have been the enemy of African pastoralists since time immemorial, for their very existence is not only a constant threat to the lives of sheep, goats and treasured cattle, but also to the safety of the herders protecting them.

The Maasai have always hunted down lion with spears, either in retribution for predated livestock, or as an important rite of passage from adolescence into moran[31] status. Although now illegal, killing a lion this way bestows a certain prestige on the perpetrators, who rarely face serious reprisals. Safari operators such as Tristan pay the Maasai to use their land on the understanding that lion living there are to be preserved; in return, victims of genuine livestock predation would be fairly compensated for their loss. Despite this, there were occasionally breaches that incensed Tristan, who deplored the gratuitous killings and believed the destruction of a lion was akin to slaying the goose that lays the golden egg.

A year after the IUCN listing, Tristan took a group of clients that included Anthony and Georgi Wickham for a game drive at dusk to look for his favourite pride at Olare Orok. They found them sprawled out beneath the shade of a fever tree less than a mile upstream from camp, where a contented lioness lay on her side a short distance away from the others, whilst fat tawny cubs with round bat-ears tumbled back and forth over her full belly. The Land Rover was parked close enough for guests

---

31 Maasai warrior.

to see her stomach palpitating gently in the evening sunshine, as Tristan quietly explained the pride hierarchy, and the challenges facing a suckling lioness permanently in need of food.

Guests left camp early the following morning, riding up the shaded lugga[32] valley past hilltops glowing beneath the rising sun, but there was not an animal to be seen anywhere. Tristan was puzzled by the scarcity of wildlife, but after thirty minutes riding heard a metallic whisper in the distance, which grew in volume and intensity as he led the group at a canter towards the noise.

'We arrived, and there it was – the source of the cacophony,' Georgi Wickham recalled years later. 'There were Maasai warriors in front of us dressed in full ceremonial gear, some with impressive headdress, some carrying spears, and walking in a sort of beating line, battering on tins and making an almighty ruckus. It felt like we had ridden into a movie set.'

Tristan realised they had arrived at the closing stages of a Maasai lion hunt and rode up to remonstrate with the warriors in Swahili. 'I didn't know exactly what he was saying,' Georgi remembered, 'but the meaning was abundantly clear in anyone's language.' At this moment her horse, whose scarred hindquarters bore witness to a previous lion attack, whipped around and came face to face with a lioness crouched on her belly. She was panting heavily, white teeth prominent from a half-opened mouth, her face crinkled in a snarl.

The warriors surrounding the stricken lion now turned their attention on Tristan, screaming abuse and thrusting their spears aggressively towards him. Georgi remembers thinking that the scenario was spinning rapidly and dangerously out of control, when Tristan pulled his horse round, and urging the others to follow, galloped home to radio for help.

After breakfast, the group returned to the scene in a Land Rover. The sun was high enough to have banished the heavy dew and dried the rustling brown grass, but the land was cloaked in eerie silence and there was not a warrior in sight. Tristan asked a Maasai woman carrying water if she had seen anyone, but she shook her head and kept walking. 'Of course, she hadn't seen anything,' Georgi remembered. 'It was like a veil was being

---

32 A watercourse or small stream.

drawn over the events of just an hour earlier.'

Tristan led the way to a clearing in the scrub, where they found the lioness lying on her side. Her eyes wore the lifeless glaze of death, and two dark red stumps marked the places where her long tail and front foot had been hacked from her body. Beneath her belly, pale circles of skin surrounding each wrinkled teat shone bare and worn from the ravenous attention of cubs now facing death. As the group walked back to the Land Rover in silence, several vultures that had been gliding overhead came winging down to earth and started to hop on ungainly black legs towards the corpse.

The death of a suckling lioness from the Olare Orok pride that Tristan was in the process of habituating to horses and people troubled him deeply; paradoxically, however, he was a lifelong advocate of putting the welfare of the species ahead of the plight of an individual. This unsentimental and pragmatic approach meant that Tristan thoroughly approved of and endorsed licensed hunting, provided the subsequent revenue was returned to habitat preservation and conservation.

Later in life, as the part owner of a wildlife-friendly ranch in northern Kenya, Tristan deplored the fact that certain animals could be legally killed in the interests of farming and conservation, but that landowners were not permitted to benefit by charging someone for the privilege of carrying out a necessary cull.

With the exception of bird shooting, all commercial hunting had been banned in Kenya since 1973, but Tristan was convinced selective culling of certain species would have been a much better way forward than an outright ban. Although ambivalent about hunting with a rifle, he knew that countries such as Tanzania and South Africa, which permitted licensed hunting, benefited from significant revenues being channelled back into conservation.

He also resented the different approach to wildlife stewardship adopted by South Africa, where all game belonged to the landowner, and Kenya, where the wildlife was owned by the government. Tristan found nothing contradictory about these views with his 1995 appointment as an Honorary Game Warden to KWS, the Kenya Wildlife Service, an organisation that had been established six years earlier with the mandate to conserve and manage wildlife in Kenya, and to enforce related laws and regulations.

When local Maasai approached Tristan with news of a sick buffalo in February 1997, he agreed to dispatch the injured beast, and as Martyn Lee was on safari with him at the time, insisted that his best man should take the shot. The buffalo belonged to a small group of old dugga bulls that had taken to hiding up by day in the thick, thorny hillside of Oloiburmut, which lies a short distance from the campsite at Olare Lamun.

Climbing the steep hill on foot is a highlight of staying at this camp, for the views from the summit are far-reaching and spectacular in every direction. Having followed a winding path to the top, guests sit beneath the shade of fig trees, or lie back amongst warm rocks, to scour the thorn-dimpled plains beneath them for game. A search through binoculars reveals an extraordinary diversity of wildlife, ranging from the rock hyraxes and klipspringers that live on the hilltop itself, to elephant, buffalo, giraffe and smaller savannah game dotted about a green canvas untouched by the hand of man.

Tristan said that to sit and absorb the timeless wanderings of wildlife from such a natural gallery felt like being on the roof of heaven, and left instructions for his remains to be scattered here amongst the ragged, rocky ridge of Oloiburmut after his death.

Tristan knew it would be suicidally dangerous to search an impenetrable hillside for a buffalo whose painful condition would encourage an unprovoked attack on humans. The existence of an injured buffalo on the hill also made an ascent with safari clients too risky to contemplate whilst the animal was still at large. The bulls had been spotted several times, grazing at first light on the grassy plains that run away from the steep, eastern flank of Oloiburmut, and Tristan's proposal was to hide there before sunrise and ambush the bachelor group as they returned to their daytime resting place. For the plan to succeed, Tristan and Martyn also needed to be downwind of their quarry, so the buffalo could not smell human scent on the breeze; it would be game over if any of them got wind of their pursuers.

As the two men waited patiently for sunrise amongst a tangle of thorns, the sound of herbivores chomping grass close to their hiding place mingled with a swelling chorus of birdsong. Trees and rocks gradually assumed shape and colour, as light seeped into the landscape to reveal the ghostly silhouettes of feeding gazelle, and beyond them four shapeless dark blurs on the plain.

As the bulls approached, Tristan and Martyn could see their sagging briskets lapping the dewy grass, and discern one trailing the others with his head low to the ground. When they reached the foot of Oloiburmut, the three healthy bulls walked straight into the safety of dense scrub, but the last one paused, broadside on, as he contemplated the best way into the thicket. Two more steps and he would disappear from sight.

'It's now or never,' Tristan whispered into his friend's ear. A split second later, Martyn squeezed the trigger and the roar of the .375 rifle rolled out like a wave to send game fleeing in every direction. Watching through his binoculars, Tristan heard the wallop of a bullet smacking home, but lost sight of the buffalo as it vanished into thick scrub. He knew it would be madness to move for several minutes, for heart-shot buffalo can live long enough to find and kill their pursuer before the lethal bullet takes effect.

During the long, unnerving silence that followed his shot, Martyn felt a light tap on his shoulder, and without moving a muscle, followed the line of Tristan's gaze across fifty yards of undergrowth to the buffalo glaring straight at them from above. His huge bulk was swaying gently from side to side as blood pattered softly onto a mat of dead leaves.

The old bull had sunk the wind[33] until he found the scent of his hunters, and then stalked silently upwind to finish them off. Martyn lifted the big rifle slowly to his shoulder and took careful aim through the open sights; this time the buffalo went down instantly. They waited several minutes before walking in to the body, keeping the rifle loaded just in case. When Tristan touched long black eyelashes there was no flicker of life, just a festering wound between the boss of forty-five-inch horns bubbling with yellow pus and smothered in small black flies.

That night guests at Olare Lamun Camp dined on buffalo fillet, and for days afterwards camp staff feasted on the rich meat. The magnificent horns

---

33 A hunting term for moving downwind, usually by the quarry so that it can smell the scent of its pursuer.

were taken back to Deloraine, where they hung on the veranda for many years, before Tristan stashed them into his luggage and took them back to England as a present for his best man.

CHAPTER ELEVEN

Life on Safari

MOST Offbeat riding safari clients arrived into Nairobi on an early morning flight, where they were met by Tristan or Mark Laurence and taken for breakfast in the fashionable suburb of Karen, before the five-hour journey to the Mara. They crossed the fertile Kikuyu Highlands in Land Rovers, before dropping two thousand feet onto the volcano-studded floor of the Great Rift Valley for a picnic lunch. The journey continued with a climb out over the Mau Escarpment to the east and on past the Maasai capital of Narok – the last town between Nairobi and the Masai Mara – to the first campsite beside a stream flowing beneath a grove of yellow-barked fever trees at the foot of the Loita Hills.

No glossy brochure or promotional video could prepare clients for the magical beauty and intimate setting of this campsite, where the air at six thousand feet felt crisp and clean and Meru-style tents were shaded by tall trees. Many guests were surprised by the absence of mosquitoes and other biting insects, which are rare interlopers at high altitude. Smiling camp staff appeared as if by magic to offer the new arrivals refreshments, and carry their luggage to tents kitted out with comfortable raised twin beds, carpets, and bedside tables supplied with water, glasses and a torch. Canvas wash basins stood on spindly legs beneath the awning either side of each tent's entrance, which was marked at night by the flickering glow of a paraffin lamp.

After everyone had finished unpacking, Tristan gathered them up for a tour of the camp, explaining how everything worked and introducing them to bush showers and long-drop loos. Water for the showers was heated in a big drum above a wood fire, and then poured by camp staff into large canvas bags operated on a pulley system with a sprinkler at the bottom. Guests were notified once their shower was ready, so all they had to do was step up onto the wooden decking inside the booth and pull down a lever, releasing five blissful minutes of piping hot water to wash away the dust and dirt of the bush.

Each tent was supplied with its own freshly dug long-drop loo inside the privacy of a small cubicle, and a seat supported by a four-legged wooden stool fixed carefully above the latrine. Tristan ended his talk by explaining that hot water bottles were available for the cool Kenyan nights and dirty boots left outside a tent in the evening would be returned polished and clean by dawn the next morning.

In later years, scheduled or charter flights into one of the Mara's bush airstrips delivered clients in time for lunch, but there was still enough daylight for an evening ride or walk for those arriving much later by vehicle. Having showered and freshened up after their first introduction to the African bush, guests gathered around an open-air fire, where they were offered ice-cold drinks and nibbles by camp staff. Tristan was always the last to shower, and his late arrival at the fireside precipitated a flurry of activity from gappies anxious to avoid a public dressing down, should the boss notice anyone with an empty glass.

Slender Maasai warriors draped in colourful robes sometimes appeared before dinner to entertain guests to a performance of traditional dancing and singing, at which members of the audience were often invited to join in. Later in the week, there would be an opportunity to visit a Maasai village made from mud, sticks and cattle dung, and gain an insight into their fascinating pastoral lifestyle.

Tristan seated guests personally for dinner, served by a head waiter from the Wakamba[34] tribe called Timothy inside the mess tent, or on warm evenings outside beneath the stars. They were frequently astonished by the superb food African staff prepared with the most basic facilities over a natural fire; the first course might be smoked sailfish from the Indian Ocean, followed by beef from the ranching country up north, with a

---

34 The Wakamba (or Kamba) people are a Bantu ethnic group or tribe, who live in the semi-arid formerly Eastern Province of Kenya stretching east from Nairobi to Tsavo and north up to Embu, Kenya.

fresh fruit salad to finish. Birthdays were celebrated by the gift of a round cake covered in thick icing, which the recipient was encouraged to slice open with a sharp knife, much to the amusement of anyone who knew the cake was made from dried elephant dung that is almost impossible to cut.

Although provisions were replenished during the ride with local produce, most of the supplies were packed with dry ice into cool boxes by the Karen Provision Stores in Nairobi. Tristan insisted on controlling all catering arrangements in his efforts to perfect the gastronomic experience; menus were planned meticulously and staff forbidden from opening a cool box ahead of its date. He disapproved of water in plastic containers, and as an alternative, encouraged clients to drink spring water transported from Deloraine in specially adapted tanks beneath the horse lorry.

The end of a lively dinner signalled the start of more entertainment, which often lasted until the small hours. Because Tristan's camps were in private concessions, national park rules forbidding night drives did not apply, which meant that game-viewing opportunities could be extended long after sunset. Although not compulsory, most found it impossible to resist their guide's infectious enthusiasm for a post-dinner game drive, and the chance of seeing nocturnal wildlife from the specially adapted roof of a long-wheelbase Land Rover. A lion hunt played out in the beam of a powerful spotlight was the ultimate prize, but passengers also spotted elusive serval cats, shuffling porcupine, the reflected orange eyes of bush babies sparkling from thorn trees, and spring hares bounding like miniature kangaroos. Hours later, the tourists fell asleep in their tents to a backdrop of unfamiliar noises, learning during the week to identify the lion's strangulated roar from the eerie whoop of hyenas, or the saw-like rasp of a leopard. At the Mara River campsite, grunting hippos wandered around camp at night, terrifying light sleepers by chomping grass noisily within feet of their tent, and occasionally decorating the canvas with a spray of sloppy green manure.

On nights when the Land Rovers stayed in camp, everyone sat around the fire with a drink in hand, and if lucky, were treated to one of Tristan's word-perfect poetry recitals. His favourites were two lengthy ballads with themes close to his heart. 'The Man from Snowy River' describes a young

Australian stockman's triumph in rounding up a stallion that had escaped to join wild bush horses in Australia's rugged Snowy Mountains, and is a stirring tale of adversity overcome with a distinct David and Goliath theme. 'The Fox's Prophecy' is remarkable for the accurate predictions made by a fox from the English Cotswolds in the late nineteenth century, including a rise of liberalism at odds with Tristan's own strongly held conservative beliefs.

Tristan's performance was sometimes followed by Timothy's poignant rendition of 'Malaika', a timeless Kenyan love song, although the waiter became less keen on singing in public after old age had robbed him of most of his teeth. One safari assistant remembers that fireside chat was also a time when guests 'learned more about the game and birds, as well as Kenya politics and what was wrong with the world; Tristan made you think about things that you normally wouldn't have noticed.' Man's overpopulation of the planet was a core theme in these late-night discussions, and Tristan never failed to remind his audience how rapidly Kenya's population had expanded from just two million inhabitants when the great railway from Mombasa to Lake Victoria was completed in 1901.

However much he enjoyed putting the world to right in front of a captive audience, Tristan disliked telling stories of his own exploits, unless the mood and personalities were right. He was a good listener, however, being genuinely interested in other people's lives, homes and families. As a result, many of his clients went home having made a new friend during their Kenyan safari.

Guests were woken at dawn with a cup of tea, the tinkle of water being poured into their washbasin, the soft rumble of African voices, and the sweet sound of birdsong. On days when the safari moved to a new campsite, bags had to be packed ready for loading in good time, after which riders made up their own picnic lunch from ingredients left out by kitchen staff. On non-moving days, they enjoyed an early morning ride before returning to a sumptuous breakfast of local fruit, freshly baked bread and a full-blown fry-up with the eggs cooked to order.

As moving days involved riding up to thirty miles across country, guests were encouraged to make their way to the horse lines as soon as possible after breakfast, where syces waited patiently with their charges tacked up and ready. Great care was taken to match horse and rider according to information provided when booking the holiday; nervous ones were provided with quiet mounts, while experienced riders were given forward-going horses that preferred to be at the front. Everyone rode in English saddles[35] and was provided with a water bottle and a saddle bag in which to carry a picnic lunch and other essentials, such as sun cream, cameras and binoculars. Riders were advised to wear neutral colours on safari; their guide favoured a worn-out shirt with sleeves rolled down to nut-brown wrists and hands, blue jeans, polished leather chaps, and a baseball hat as sun-bleached and faded as the rest of his attire.

Guests on a typical Offbeat riding safari spent a week exploring the bush between the first campsite in the Loita Hills and the ride's furthest point west of the Siria Escarpment. No two days were ever the same as the group meandered through thickets of wait-a-bit thorn, searched hidden valleys for elephant, and careered full pelt across wide savannah plains. Riders soon realised that Tristan's quietly spoken words 'time for a little canter' were a prelude to long and exhilarating gallops amongst herds of snorting wildebeest, or upsides statuesque giraffe, floating effortlessly above horses racing flat to the boards.

Safari horses were adept at avoiding aardvark holes lurking like hidden traps on these long gallops, suddenly swerving or changing legs to avoid a tumble, but were occasionally brought down in a crashing fall. Horse and rider were usually unharmed, but not always. The leading Irish National Hunt trainer, Jessie Harrington, suffered a broken neck when her mount tripped up in 2005. Like many others who suffered broken legs, collar bones and arms over the years, she made a full recovery.

Although riders were not expected to overtake their guide, Tristan adopted a relaxed and informal attitude to safari protocol, which was the antithesis of boring nose-to-tail trail riding. His charges were allowed to ride several abreast, take their own line away to one flank, or drop out at the rear with the reserve horses that accompanied every ride. This casual

---

35 English saddles are different to the heavy, trail-riding saddles used on many riding holidays around the world. They are easier on the horses and designed for the rider to stand up in the saddle when cantering or galloping, to relieve weight from the horse's back.

approach concealed a constant awareness of potential danger that, once identified, inspired confidence in all who rode behind him.

'Tristan was a fascinating guide, great fun, but also very safe to ride with,' an admirer recalled. 'He informed us about wildlife with a mix of military and Attenborough style, before encouraging us to observe in silence without imparting further unnecessary knowledge or showing off.' Guests rode with a heightened sense of anticipation, never knowing what treat or danger lay around the next corner; perhaps a leopard sunbathing on a rocky ledge, a bull buffalo glaring malevolently from the scrub, or maybe tall Maasai herders leaning nonchalantly on their spears.

Sometimes horses indicated the presence of dangerous game before any human by quivering nervously when they scented lion hidden amongst thick scrub, or tensing in anticipation of a charge at the smell of elephants, browsing upwind but out of sight. Each horse wore a rope headcollar over its leather bridle, so it could be tied up during lunch breaks, but the most trusted were simply untacked and turned loose to graze wherever they pleased.

Saddlebag picnics were substituted for cold drinks and a salad buffet when lunches were supported by Land Rover; afterwards there was always time for a siesta, and a refreshing swim if lunching beside the Mara River or her tributaries. During late afternoon or early evening, Tristan led the group into a new campsite, where they discovered the same tents and facilities of the previous night magically re-created, having been dismantled by camp staff and transported twenty or thirty miles by vehicle.

The different campsites visited during a riding safari held their own unique attractions. The first site beneath the Loita Hills was abandoned when tin huts started to appear in the vicinity and was replaced by Olare Lamun, where a spring-fed stream flows through short, grassy plains. The next camp at Olare Orok nearly forty miles away is known for its large pride of resident lion, and the chance to spot an elusive leopard in the eponymous gorge nearby. Hippo and crocodile are the highlight of camping beside the Mara River, and there is still the chance of finding rhino in the superb game country beneath the final campsite on top of the Siria Escarpment, where the views spread east to Tanzania and west to the faint outline of the Loita Hills.

Journeys between camps are always undertaken on' horseback, but on non-moving days, game drives with Land Rovers into the Masai Mara National Reserve give both the horses and riders a well-earned break. Evening game drives invariably wind up at a vantage point for a sundowner,[36] where the sight of a spectacular if short-lived sunset can be enjoyed with a drink to hand.

Adventurous clients also enjoy leaping over trees which have been knocked down by elephant, a diversion encouraged by Tristan, who had every confidence in horses that had been educated to jump properly back at Deloraine. When he came across a playground of fallen timber during the closing minutes of the final day of an action-packed safari in August 1995, Tristan could not resist one last thrill, and led the way on Tangawizi over a succession of testing obstacles.

Perhaps tired by the exertions of a long day, the liver chestnut gelding failed to clear a large tree and turned a complete somersault, breaking Tristan's leg beneath a heavy fall. One of the guests on the ride, Bill Vanderfelt, remembers the bone of a severe double fracture protruding through Tristan's blood-soaked jeans as he attempted to make the patient comfortable. Bill left two young men from his party to take care of Tristan, and with the rest of the group followed the Mara River upstream back to camp, which they reached safely after an anxious thirty minutes.

Meanwhile Tristan's companions had fixed up a makeshift splint to ease his pain, but their matches were too damp to light a fire and indicate their position to the search party arranged by Bill. They watched the Land Rover's headlights sweeping the bush for nearly twenty minutes before the rescuers eventually found them and frightened off hyenas that had been closing in under the cover of darkness.

Tristan was transported slowly and painfully back to camp, where he was made as comfortable as possible for the long night ahead. 'When we got to open Tristan's medical kit, it looked like something that had been buried with an Egyptian mummy,' Bill remembers. 'Fortunately, my wife and I had put together a state-of-the-art kit and I would like to think that

---

36 A safari experience where guests stop at a vantage point for a drink at sunset. The sun sets quickly on the equator so sundowners rarely last for more than half an hour.

the antiseptic powder, antibiotics, bandages et al. saved Tristan's leg. He did request a bottle of whisky as well, which *à contre-coeur* we felt obliged to give him; the pain must have been excruciating.'

They eventually got through to the Flying Doctor Service in Nairobi and arranged for an evacuation from the local airstrip at 8.00 a.m. the following morning. Having helped load Tristan into the plane, Bill Vanderfelt and his friends returned by Land Rover to Deloraine, but visited their guide in hospital before flying home. They found him 'looking like something Dr Frankenstein had put together, with his leg full of pins, nuts and bolts; but very much alive.'

Tristan once more described his ordeal in a typically understated fashion: 'Fall from Tangawizi. Break leg. Dreadful night but flying doctors etc.' After the Italian surgeon and traumatologist, Alberto Bencivenga, had pinned the leg back together, Tristan was confined to the Aga Khan Hospital in Nairobi for another ten days before he was allowed home.

Although he was ready for a return to the saddle by the end of the year, Tristan's leg was slow to mend, and the plates were not removed for another fifteen months. As he wanted to join friends for lunch in the Muthaiga Club afterwards, Tristan declined a general anaesthetic in favour of a local one, which resulted in a severely painful operation.

'The plate had become embedded in his leg, so they had to hack away at it with a hammer and chisel,' Cindy remembers. 'What should have been a straightforward thirty-minute procedure ended up taking two-and-a-half hours. Tristan said he had never known such pain.' The wound would not stop bleeding during lunch after the operation, and when Tristan's shoe welled up with blood, his wife took him outside to change the dressing. The leg never fully recovered and was intermittently sore for the rest of his life.

Offbeat Safaris would have struggled to honour safari bookings in the months following Tristan's accident without the help of Mark Laurence, who had been allocated an experienced Maasai syce called Metian to show him the routes between campsites. Metian began his career working for Tony Church in the early eighties, but left Safaris Unlimited at the same time as Tristan and became an important member of the Offbeat team. The cadaverous Maasai had contracted polio as a child, which left him with a permanent limp, and such a weak right hand that he always held the reins in his good left hand when riding.

Metian's English had progressed little beyond the words 'yes', 'no', and 'enough' since the day Tristan first met him in 1983, which conveniently absolved him from having to speak to foreigners, although he was happy to chatter away to Mark in Swahili. He was wary of dangerous big game and avoided close encounters with elephants whenever possible, repeating the words, 'enough, enough, enough,' while riding away in the opposite direction. He was frequently astonished by the risks white men and women took on safari, and as Metian had never learnt to swim, he sometimes refused to cross the Mara River on horseback. However, he knew his way around the Mara landscape backwards, and was an invaluable help to Mark Laurence.

After Tristan's return to guiding towards the end of 1995, Mark's employment allowed two riding safaris to be run concurrently during a time of increasing popularity and demand. Mark remembers the years leading up to the terrorist attack on New York in September 2001, which temporarily put many American clients off travelling, as an era when 'we absolutely worked our butts off on back-to-back safaris.' Clients during these years included prominent names from the racing world, such as leading trainers Michael Stoute, James Fanshawe, and Luca Cumani, whose daughter Francesca spent a season working for Offbeat. Support for Offbeat Safaris from the British horse-racing community continued so strongly that, within a few years, Tristan was able to note in a letter to Rufus that the winning trainers of both the English Derby and the Oaks had joined him on safari.

However, not all clients were to Tristan's taste. He found a few, like the businessman who asked what animal a wildebeest preys on, immensely irritating, and was occasionally moved to intervene over sheer bad manners. An assistant remembers him angrily boiling over at breakfast after three greedy clients ate all the toast, and again when the same men sat in the Land Rover without offering to help, as others tried to push the vehicle out of a bog.

Some clients in turn criticised their guide for shortcomings similar to those penned by the Bostonian a decade earlier, but compliments heavily outnumbered the complaints. Many wrote glowing letters of thanks after returning home. One woman described her 1998 safari as a 'fondly remembered life-changing adventure'; others complimented the excellent staff and organisation, superb horses and skill of the guides. Mark Laurence also came in for his share of praise, an American writing that he was the 'difference between a great trip and an Incredible Life Experience.'

Most clients only met Cindy when they returned to Deloraine at the end of their safari, but were much taken by her calm efficiency and attention to detail; few realised the hard work and time she devoted behind the scenes to booking and organising their holiday. Tristan overcame his objection to comments in the visitors' book at Deloraine, where adjectives such as epic, sensational and memorable crop up with unfailing frequency. Bill Vanderfelt remembers Tristan's kindness and humour when his son, who was a novice rider, fell off each time his mount shied at francolin[37] taking wing. After the third time Tristan threw the embarrassed young man a big grin and told him, 'Okay, Christophe, you can stop showing off now.'

Letters of thanks often included an open invitation for the Voorspuys to come and stay on their next visit to America, Britain or Ireland. There were so many offers that Tristan and Cindy could have spent months, if not years, taking them all up; those they found time to visit were delighted to be hosting the glamorous young couple from Africa that everyone wanted to meet. The Voorspuys were generous guests, bringing out special presents from Kenya, such as solid brass ashtrays cast from the print of a lion's pad, which replicated the Offbeat logo of the same footprint framed within a lucky horseshoe. Trips to Ireland, Lambourn and Newmarket for the big race meetings, and invitations to stay at fabulous country estates such as Melbury in Dorset, were enormous fun and an opportunity to recruit more clients.

Running a successful safari business also garnered some unusual perks, including an invitation to join Count Konrad Goess-Saurau's private party aboard Rovos Rail in South Africa, which claims to be the most luxurious train in the world. Days were spent shooting African game birds on private ranches, and nights given over to formal dinners, where the male guests

---

37 A type of African gamebird, similar to a partridge.

wore black tie and their wives dressed in long gowns 'with pearls down to their knees'.

Although Offbeat Safaris had established a global reputation, Tristan realised his business could not prosper on word of mouth alone, and the off-season rainy months of November, April and May were dedicated to marketing trips to Europe and the USA. These included a first visit to the Badminton Horse Trials in Gloucestershire in April 1996, where operators similar to the Voorspuys from Botswana, South Africa and Malawi formed the African Horse Safari Association (AHSA) and pooled resources to take a trade stand for the purpose of entertaining existing clients and recruiting new ones.

Badminton was so successful that Offbeat Safaris have returned every year since, and the AHSA stand has become something of a mecca for anyone who has ever ridden with Offbeat. Names of respected tour operators start to appear in the diaries too; a handful took their own stands at Badminton, but whenever Tristan was in the UK, he visited as many travel companies as possible to drum up support for the business.

These prosperous years were also blighted by disasters of varying magnitude, but tales of misadventure and derring-do only served to escalate Offbeat Safaris' growing reputation as the experience of a lifetime. The chaotic 1996 Christmas safari, which took place soon after the plate had been removed from Tristan's leg, is remembered as being one of the worst.

The trip started happily with two separate groups guided by Tristan and Mark sharing facilities at Olare Lamun, after which Tristan's group set off ahead of the others, but when they returned to their new camp after a game drive on Christmas Eve, all the horses had vanished. Mark arrived shortly afterwards to explain that his horses had also broken loose and joined the others to form a large herd that had galloped off into the bush.

Nine horses made their way back to Olare Lamun across country, where Mark found them later the same evening. Early on Christmas morning, volunteers from both groups combined to ride what had grown to sixteen horses back to camp, while Satima and Daybreak returned having been ambushed and badly mauled by lion. Several more had been recovered by sunset, but the mood at camp changed when a car drove up carrying a badly injured Metian, who had left earlier for Narok to refuel the pick-up.

The vehicle had overturned on the way home and trapped Metian between its undercarriage and the hard dirt road. His shoulder was broken in the accident, and if an upturned loo roll had not acted like a jack to support the vehicle a few inches above ground, his skull would have been instantly crushed. When Metian's rescuers found him, he had been held prisoner for more than an hour, but they managed to extract the Maasai and drive him back to Olare Orok, where Tristan unsuccessfully attempted to pop his dislocated shoulder back into place. Metian ended up having a long but successful operation at the Aga Khan Hospital in Nairobi, but it was several months before he was able to return to work.

By Boxing Day there were enough horses for everyone to enjoy a ride, and by nightfall the following day, all bar one of the twenty-three missing horses had been recovered, including the grey gelding, Blizzard, who was found on top of the escarpment having swum the Mara River. But a mare named Maria never returned and was presumed to have been killed and eaten by lion.

⁺ CHAPTER TWELVE ⁺

A Nice Place to Live

THE VOORSPUYS had set about the daunting task of breathing life into Deloraine as soon as they moved in. One of their first jobs was to remove yards of dusty wire netting that had protected the upstairs veranda from bats, and utilise the space at each end to provide two more bedrooms and bathrooms. The tired seventies décor was given a comprehensive makeover, and some large pieces of furniture including two chaise longues, huge mirrors and Dutch marquetry were imported from Folkington to complement the pieces that Pam left behind. Furnishing such a large house was a formidable challenge for its new tenants, and shortly before their move, Tristan asked his friend, Chris Wilson, to bid on his behalf for a huge dining-room table being sold at auction in Nairobi.

After a weekend at Deloraine without water, electricity, or wood for the fire, Tristan doubted that he could afford the costs of refurbishing and running the house, but was unable to contact Chris and cancel the bid. When told of his success, Tristan announced with an air of resignation that there could not possibly be any turning back now, for only Deloraine had a large enough dining-room to accommodate the expensive antique.

Recognising their important historical value, Tristan had the original family portraits of Deloraine's founders, Lady Eileen and Lord Francis Scott, professionally copied before they were shipped back to England. Cindy managed to track down seven pairs of light sconces that had graced the drawing-room, dining-room and bedrooms, and restore them to their original positions in the house. In the fullness of time, oil paintings of both Tristan and Cindy were commissioned and hung alongside those of the property's former owners in the dining-room, and a large gilt mirror replaced the de László portrait above the fireplace.

Most people on an Offbeat riding safari spend two nights at Deloraine at the beginning or end of their ride, which is also the recommended stay for other paying guests on a personalised itinerary. The five-hour-long drive to Deloraine for those returning from the Mara passes through bustling African villages and the high tea country of Kericho, where the air is often chilly and the undulating hills are carpeted in rows of orderly green tea plants.

After the long journey and a week in the bush, guests especially appreciate the comforts of Deloraine, where deep baths replace bush showers, and the spacious rooms smell faintly of leather and polish. House guests gather for a drink before dinner in the large drawing-room, where logs crackle from the grate of the enormous stone fireplace, and the party is often swelled by neighbours invited to help entertain the visitors. Anyone unaware of their hosts' vocation would quickly realise from the selection of framed photographs adorning every surface of this room that the Voorspuys' lifestyle revolved around horses, family and safaris.

A bell is rung to announce that dinner is ready in the dining-room next door, where the dress is usually casual, although a man who appeared with holes in his shirt was sent upstairs to change by his host, and anyone attempting to sit down wearing a baseball cap or T-shirt could expect the same short shrift.

The downstairs veranda is a natural focal point, where house dogs bask in the early morning sunshine and greet each breakfast arrival by thumping tails loudly against warm wooden floorboards. Deloraine has been home to many dogs since Tristan brought Bertie the Border Terrier with him from The Roost, including Labradors, Staffordshire Bull Terriers, and several other Borders. Being self-assured, fiercely independent and unconditionally affectionate, they were a little different to most dogs in England. Many met a grisly end on safari. Some like poor Bertie were killed by other dogs, and at least two were poisoned on the mountain by poachers. Very few of the Deloraine dogs made it to ripe old age, but they were as integral to the fabric of life there as the children, horses and staff.

A library at the south end of the veranda housed books describing military conflicts around the globe, and Tristan's extensive collection of weather-beaten baseball hats. A wooden door at the opposite end leads

Left: Henk and Pearl's wedding, March 1947.

Below left: Henk in uniform.

Below right: A young Tristan.

Above: The Voorspuy family in 1959 near Bexhill-on-Sea, Sussex (Tristan on far right).

Below left: Tristan competing in a hunter trial as a young boy.

Below right: Tristan in early life.

Left: Tristan at the Mill, Umberleigh 1977.

Below: Tristan and friends on typically hard-drinking form, Lulworth 1976. From left to right: Jamie Howard, Tim Thomson-Jones, Tristan, Geoff Carey, Peter Wisher and Guy Hanmer (seated).

Top: Officers of the Blues and Royals in 1977. Tristan top row, second from right.

Below: Hunting with the Weser Vale Bloodhounds while stationed with the army in Germany (Tristan on far left).

Above: Tristan on the bike ride from Sussex to Cape Town in 1982.

Below: Rosslyn, the Ryrie family home in Nairobi.

Above: Tristan with Elizabeth Ryrie, Tana River, Kenya 1986.

Below: The aftermath of the Land Cruiser crash, Lake Bogoria 1984.

Tristan and Cindy's wedding, May 1989

Above: Tristan with Johnny Camm on safari in Uganda, February 1994.

Below left: Tristan and Roland Purcell prepare to fly his new Cessna 206 from Buckinghamshire to Kenya, May 1994.

Below right: Tristan (on elephant) with Rory Hensman at Braeside, July 1998.

Above: The front of Deloraine House.

Below: Ginger Bell's hounds meet at Deloraine, October 2001.

Above: Tristan enjoying a safari in the Okavango Delta, Botswana in June 2016.

Right: View of Kilimanjaro taken during the first Amboseli ride, 2004.

Below: Offbeat Safaris campsite beside the Mara River, with guest tents overlooking the river and with bush showers in the foreground.

Above: Tristan riding Cancan on safari in the Mara, September 2008.

Above right: Jakob von Plessen with Nettie, the Maasai spotter in 2013.

Right: Mark Laurence on safari in the Mara, July 2007.

Below: The Voorspuy family with Tristan's plane at Sosian, 2006.

Above: Tristan with Sean Outram at Sosian, October 2010.

Left: Topper, Tristan's favourite border terrier and a regular on safari, was a tragic victim of the 2009 lorry crash.

Below: Tristan, a registered stud bull that helped establish the Sosian herd of baron cattle in 2007.

Above: Tristan leading a safari group across the Mara River, June 2014.

Below: Tristan sizing up an elephant on safari in the Mara, June 2014.

Above: Tristan with Archie, Imo and Jack the Labrador on safari in the Mara, August 2015.

Left: The Voorspuy family on safari in the Mara on New Year's Day 2017, ten weeks prior to Tristan's murder.

Below: Tristan with Sorrell, Morven and Rufus at Thady Voorspuy's wedding, 2016.

Above: Positive relationships with the local Maasai were crucial to running a successful safari business and achieving conservation goals.

Below: Sosian wildlife targeted by land invaders in early 2017; the three month old elephant that was rescued and successfully re-homed.

Above: The charred remains of Richard Constant's house at Sosian in October 2017, seven months after it was burned down.

Below: Archie and Nettie at Tristan's final resting place, Oliburnmunt close to Olare Lamun in the Mara, March 2017.

into the office, and breakfast was sometimes disturbed by the host's heated telephone conversations from within. 'At Deloraine, Tristan was in the office mostly, growling,' one helper remembers.

Up to forty staff from the head syce to the humble mole catcher formed an orderly line on the lawn outside the office window to collect their wages from Tristan every month, including a man in charge of the donkey and firewood cart, cooks, carpenters, mechanics, gardeners and askari night watchmen. Some members of staff, such as housekeepers Jane, Margret and Joyce, have been at Deloraine since the days of Pam Scott, while others such as the indomitable Beatrice came with the Voorspuys from Nairobi. Beatrice is no longer on the payroll, but is remembered for her disconcerting habit of nudging guests sharply in the ribs if they failed to pay attention when she was serving them dinner.

At the bottom of the gardens, a plot was cultivated to supply the house with fresh produce, prepared in the same tiny kitchen equipped with some of the same basic facilities that catered for royal guests in the 1930s, although the paraffin-fired refrigerator has now been replaced with gas and electric versions. A charcoal oven is still used for baking bread and roasting joints of meat, hand-washed clothes continue to be pressed with a charcoal iron, and Wilfreda still separates milk from a pair of Jersey house cows into thick cream every morning. Ancient Tanganyikan boilers, fed by fallen timber gathered from the estate, still heat water for much of the house, and the Deloraine plumbing remains a frequent topic of conversation; there have been numerous occasions when pipes burst without warning or the whisky-coloured water was either too hot or too cold to take a bath, but the installation of a solar system in 2002 reduced reliance on the diesel generator.

In the grounds outside, the Voorspuys made numerous improvements. The tennis court was restored with nailed-down string, instead of white line markings that quickly fade in the sun, and fitted with a net that Freddie Menzies brought out from Wimbledon Centre Court. The Voorspuys' friend and architect, Murray Levitt, designed a swimming pool with the edges sloping gently down to the water, so that insects falling in to the pool could crawl out to safety. The pool took ten days to make and was hand-dug in one of the garden's hidden suntraps by an army of workers. 'This is the most expensive swim I will ever have,' Tristan announced, before diving into the new pool for the first time. The area quickly became a midday rendezvous for guests and usurped the veranda as the go-to place for long, lazy lunches overlooking the water.

Creating a level polo pitch from a hay field in 2006 was an equally ambitious project, which added another dimension to the Voorspuys' country estate. Cricket matches played here raised funds for the Leldet Primary School at the end of the drive, where contributions from Offbeat Safaris have paid for new classrooms and desks. An airstrip was added between stables and polo field in 2010 after Tristan commandeered a grader and some Chinese construction workers employed nearby. The earth runway was completed over the course of a weekend with advice from his friend and neighbour, Willy Potgieter, and has been put to good use ever since, despite being on the side of a sloping hill with a precariously short landing and take-off.

It is a short stroll to the stables from Deloraine house, and everyone staying overnight is encouraged to join an early morning ride into the hills. Cedar trees once dominated the lower slopes of Londiani Mountain and although a handful remain, on their way uphill riders pass the mossy stumps of many more standing like gravestones amongst the ferns. As the horses climb higher, fronds of luminous lichen trail from forest trees, and in places the passage of many cattle have worn the earth tracks down to bare rock. Clearings are quickly colonised by leleshwa shrubs after the charcoal makers have moved on, but ancient hardwoods are vanquished for several lifetimes.

The destruction of woodland to fuel illegal charcoal production, and a proliferation of poachers' snares during a period of lawlessness that followed the 2007 general elections, angered Tristan greatly. However, his position as a KWS Honorary Game Warden empowered him to protect government-owned forest from such activities and employ four armed rangers to collect snares and arrest poachers.

He also detested packs of dogs terrorising the local wildlife and saw no irony in shooting any that ventured onto the farm at Deloraine, often recording the victims in his diary: 'Easter Day 1997; shoot 2 dogs on farm,' or 'Dog shoot before lunch. Shoot one in front of poachers.' Buffalo, rhino and bongo have all vanished, but despite the deforestation and poaching, Londiani Mountain is still home to aardvark, bushbuck, colobus monkeys, red duiker, bush pig, and many species of forest bird.

Tristan's predictable rants during the ride about the inequities of illegal logging and charcoal were interspersed with knowledgeable introductions to the indigenous flora and fauna. He might stop his horse to point out the convoluted stems of a strangler fig throttling their host, or the blackened trunks of fire-resistant lucky bean trees standing unbowed above the charred remains of a forest fire.

Many years later, the tiny brown fruits from these very trees in the hills above Deloraine would be gathered up and taped to every one of the service sheets handed out at his funeral. It was here, too, amongst the lucky bean trees, that Imo discovered the first elephants to have been seen anywhere near Deloraine in her lifetime. Incredibly, the elephants appeared the day before her father died.

After an hour or so, riders arrive at a glade offering incredible views across the Rift Valley to Laikipia, a place the Voorspuys named 'Top of the World'. On clear days, it is possible to discern The Aberdare Range of mountains, where a tiny population of critically endangered bongo antelope live amongst dense bamboo forest. Tristan also pointed out landmarks closer to home: symmetrical farmed fields, the shiny main road to Nairobi, and a brown smudge representing the over-exaggerated truck stop that is Rongai town. The view beneath blue skies is still overwhelmingly green, but the wide valley floor now sparkles with greenhouses built to supply Kenya's prosperous flower-growing industry.

Tristan sometimes entertained visitors who rode to hounds back home to an early morning hunt, with a pack he had rescued from certain extinction. There were once seven registered hunts in Kenya pursuing reedbuck, a common species of antelope, whose stamina and strong scent made it an ideal quarry, but by the early 1970s there was only one left. The Nairobi-based Limuru Hunt hung on until 1977, but was forced to disband due to a shortage of country to hunt across.

The hounds were given to Ginger Bell, a hunting enthusiast from Cumbria, who had emigrated to Kenya after serving there with the British Army. He established a successful butchery in Mombasa and later bought a farm near Deloraine called Lowling, where he kennelled his hounds and renamed the hunt Ginger Bell's. His pack followed a drag on private land around the Rift Valley, Nairobi and the foothills of Mount Kenya.

The elderly Ginger Bell saw his new neighbour as the pack's future, and invited Tristan to become their huntsman two years after the Voorspuys' move to Deloraine. Despite his lack of real enthusiasm to take on board another time-consuming commitment, Tristan found it impossible to turn down an opportunity to save a sport he valued so highly, for he knew that failure to accept Ginger's offer would result in the hunt disbanding.

He set about his latest challenge with characteristic determination, and his diaries contain frequent reference to early morning exercise with the hounds and their African keepers at Lowling Farm. But things did not always go smoothly. Staff and huntsman sometimes lost control of the pack when they took off after live quarry, or even stray dogs, and since he publicly deplored the poaching of native animals, Tristan would have been hugely embarrassed if his hounds ever killed the wildlife he devoted so much energy to protecting.

Most novices would have chosen a quiet occasion for their official debut as a huntsman, but Tristan was happy to wait until the morning after Brian Macoun's marriage to Annie Furlong in October 1994. After the wedding at Brian's former family home at Fintry, two hundred guests attended a reception and glittering dinner at Deloraine. Several brought their polo ponies with them to hunt early the next morning, before the sun became too hot for the hounds' comfort, and more than fifty riders enjoyed three fast runs during which there were several dramatic falls, but no serious injuries.

Three years later, Ginger Bell died and bequeathed his hounds to Tristan, requesting the presence of their new master at his funeral in full hunt livery; he was unable to attend, but was represented by Cindy blowing the 'gone away' as Ginger slipped from his mattress into the grave. Tristan was allowed to continue using the kennels at Lowling Farm and improved the pack by importing a couple of bitches from the East Cornwall Hunt close to the Macintosh's West Country home; in the fullness of time one of them gave birth to a large litter of puppies.

Even in East Africa, the ownership of a private hunt was a costly undertaking, underwritten by dazzling hunt balls as the centrepiece of fund-raising weekends that combined cocktail parties, polo matches and equine events incorporating a home-built cross-country course. These – and other Deloraine parties such as the Raj Taj Ball – acquired a lively reputation that outsiders compared to the antics of the debauched Happy Valley set in the 1930s.

Revellers certainly shot eggs off the balcony, danced precariously on the mantelpiece above the fireplace, and pinned unsuspecting victims to the lawn with croquet hoops, but the marriages of most participants held steady, and there were definitely no murders. 'There were two highlights to hunting weekends,' remembers one of the regular participants, Charlie McConnell. 'The hunting itself and the hunt balls, which unfortunately always happened in the reverse order. This meant that even if one was lucky enough to grab a couple of hours of sleep, there was little chance of a clear head, which led to more adventures in the field than might have been the case.' Tristan's polo-playing friend of old, Johnny Camm, was more forthright, confiding 'never again' to his wife, Lucy, after a particularly hair-raising hunt in 1999 that resulted in the air evacuations of two injured riders.

Although a reporter from *Country Life* magazine in England gave Ginger Bell's Hunt a glowing write-up in 2001, initial support for hunting from polo-playing and riding friends gradually fell away, and Tristan found it increasingly difficult to find time to exercise his hounds or take them hunting. After the hunt had not met for two years, the Voorspuys realised their efforts to imitate a sport they enjoyed so much in England were never going to inspire genuine enthusiasm from more than a handful of individuals.

'Looking back, trying to replicate English hunting in Africa was a bit contrived,' Cindy says. 'Tristan kept the pack going for more than a decade, but for most of our followers it was all about the party, not the hunting.' The hunt was disbanded in 2009, and hunting with hounds in East Africa was gone forever.

Polo was much better suited to the Kenyan climate and lifestyle, and many of Tristan's friends were keen players. He had resumed a sport first played during army days by joining the Nairobi Polo Club and stabling his ponies with Johnny Camm. He later sent horses and grooms up to Timau in Laikipia each May, where he and Cindy played weekend chukkas while staying with Mandy and Jackie Kenyon at Mogwooni Ranch. After moving to Deloraine, the Voorspuys became members of the Manyatta Polo Club at Gilgil, which is only an hour's drive away and was supported by many of their closest friends.

'If we weren't on safari, we were playing polo, just like people go hunting in England,' Cindy remembers. 'It was a constant backdrop to life at Deloraine and hugely social.' Tristan's determination to play as much polo as possible is clearly spelt out in a letter he wrote to his brother Morven in November 1999. After a marketing trip to London, Tristan visited Derbyshire and Leicestershire to hunt with the Quorn and the Meynell & South Staffordshire Hunts, where both masters were clients and friends, before flying to Nairobi after three consecutive days in the saddle.

'Flew home to be met by Cindy and whisked off to polo at Gilgil for three days of nine-goal polo on our own lovely horses,' he enthused. 'Not many people have had six out of seven days like that I would care to surmise; we only won one out of the three days, but it was all close and very good polo.' Tristan also revealed that he was on track to gain Kenyan citizenship, which would absolve him from having to apply for a work permit and provide another level of security to his tenure of Deloraine. 'I have just received all the papers and will probably be a Kenyan citizen by Christmas,' he wrote. Tristan's prediction was correct, although a month premature, for his citizenship was not granted until 31st January the following year.

The Manyatta Polo Club was conveniently close to Pembroke House School, where Archie and Imo were sent to board once they were six years old, even though their father had never boarded himself. Both children were swinging polo sticks from horseback from an early age and the family were proficient enough to field a full team for the prestigious Mugs Mug Polo Tournament at Gilgil, when Archie and Imo were fifteen and thirteen years old.

Tristan became chairman of the Manyatta Polo Club, and later treasurer, even though polo had to fit in around his safari commitments.

As a member of the Kenya polo team playing off a two-goal handicap, his international career took him to tournaments in India, England, Tanzania, Uganda, South Africa and Zimbabwe. During a visit to Harare to support Cindy, representing Kenya in the ladies' polo team, Tristan bought her three silver guinea fowl designed by Patrick Mavros as a twelfth wedding-anniversary present. The much-admired ornaments now adorn the dining-room table at Deloraine, along with the eighteen grains of silver maize left from the twenty-four that originally came back from Zimbabwe.

A large number of horses were required to sustain such a diverse range of equestrian interests, and the Deloraine stables expanded rapidly after the purchase of a thoroughbred chestnut stallion called Nile Star, who ran free with the mares and set the Voorspuys on the road to equine self-sufficiency. His offspring were broken in by Cindy and trained to play polo, compete in events and go on safari, but Tristan's favourite was a rig[38] called Hotspur, who flourished after an operation to remove the hidden testicle when he was four years old. The chestnut gelding became a brilliant all-rounder, equally at home leading rides through the Mara as competing with Tristan in events where the disciplines were dressage, show jumping and cross-country.

Tristan's equine achievements were all the more remarkable considering what he called his 'Land Rover back', although it was rare to hear him utter a word of complaint about a condition he suffered from throughout life. He was diagnosed with herniated discs in 1992 and instructed by his doctor to stay in bed for a month; advice that he uncharacteristically followed, although the show went on with drinks and dinner parties in the bedroom. Tristan sometimes wore a back brace to play polo and took painkillers before every chukka, but nothing could disguise a distinctive shuffling gait that became increasingly pronounced in later life. According to close friends, Tristan's constant discomfort may have contributed to his quick temper and sporadic intolerance.

Aside from hunting, polo and safari headquarters, Deloraine was the beating heart of a special family home, and for the children, a launch pad for adventures their cousins back in England could only dream of. They

---

38 A horse with only one testicle.

were often flown to and from school at Gilgil in their father's aeroplane, and when home, they were hardly out of the saddle. Archie crossed the Mara River as an infant perched on the withers of his father's horse, and Imo joined her first riding safari when only five years old.

'I was told I could do the entire trip provided I didn't whinge,' she remembers, perhaps unaware these were the very same conditions her mother was obliged to accept before joining Tristan on board the *African Queen* fifteen years earlier. Three years later, she was catapulted like a rag doll into the Mara River when her pony tripped over during a steep descent into the water, but was soon back in the saddle none the worse for her ducking. 'He was a cool Dad,' Imo remembers, 'I've been lucky and had a very different lifestyle to most of my friends.'

Her father was aware of that, too, and occasionally questioned his children's privileged upbringing. 'Archie now has an airgun and what with trampolines, motorbikes, swimming pools, tennis courts etc. really has very little to look forward to in life, I'm afraid,' he confided to Angela Macintosh. 'I hope it doesn't spoil him.'

Because he was so often away on safari, Tristan sometimes appeared distant or preoccupied during his brief interludes at Deloraine, but was not adverse to childish pranks such as the nest of fake eggs he was asked to identify one Easter Sunday; Tristan was completely fooled by the ruse, but happily joined in with the gleeful laughter that followed his blunder. Further afield, there were magical safaris, none more fabulous than a canoeing trip down the Zambezi River with Garth Thompson and friends, when Archie and Imo were just eleven and nine years old. Not only was the official age limit fourteen, but the river opposite Mana Pools had been closed to kayaks after a crocodile plucked a young girl out of one the previous week. If this additional excitement were not enough, they camped on river beaches, tracked elephants on foot, and landed in Zambia on the opposite bank of the river.

Since Cindy was preoccupied with running the bookings, office, house and stables when Tristan was away on safari, looking after the children sometimes fell to others. Twenty-five-year-old Julieta Keene arrived from Argentina to help out in 2000 and stayed for two years. Her first impression on meeting Tristan was of 'a man on a mission, who always seemed to be brooding over something, and when riding or walking was immersed in thoughts that seemed to take him far away.' Although Julieta and the other helpers overlapping her stay were frequently 'bollocked', in her eyes Tristan was paradoxically 'a gentleman, and always polite.'

Her first job was to watch over the children during a polo match, where despite her rural upbringing on an Argentine estancia, Julieta could not believe they were allowed to run around shoeless in Africa. 'Cindy was like, "It's cool, they are fine",' she remembers. After leaving Pembroke House School, Archie and Imo were sent to board at Stowe School in Buckinghamshire, where the beautiful seven-hundred-acre grounds are a short drive from their Aunt Sorrel's house at Greens Norton. They flew home to Deloraine for longer holidays, but spent half-terms and exeat weekends with their older cousins, Tam, Toby and Dominic, who were in turn invited back to Kenya during their own holidays.

Tristan enjoyed a close relationship with his three siblings and their many children, all of whom have magical memories of time spent in Africa and at Deloraine with their uncle. In later years, some were able to return his hospitality, but Toby was quite taken aback by the generous £50 note Tristan left behind as a present after staying in his London house in 2015, even though he had actually spent the night slumped over a whisky in a nearby café having lost his key to gain entry.

At Deloraine, the Voorspuys' contribution to the close-knit community of like-minded friends was never more important than following the tragic death in 2000 of Tristan's great friend, Johnny Camm, who died of injuries sustained in an horrific gyrocopter crash and explosion. As there were no facilities to treat his severe burns in Kenya, Lucy decided to fly Johnny back to England for treatment she hoped would save his life. Word of his accident had spread amongst the expat community by the time the air ambulance took off from Wilson airport in Nairobi a day and a half later, and a large crowd gathered to see their friend off.

As the plane approached Greece the following morning, it became clear the patient needed further hospital attention, so a decision was made to land in Athens, where he could be stabilised before continuing the journey. When passing a church *en route* to hospital, Lucy noticed tubes connecting her husband to a life-support machine had become detached, and for the first time since his accident, was overwhelmed by a premonition that all might be lost.

'Having been determined that Johnny was going to make it no matter what,' Lucy remembers, 'I was suddenly overcome by a feeling that said whatever is best for Johnny, let it be. It turned out that was the moment he died.'

More than seven hundred mourners attended his funeral in Nairobi, and Tristan struck a sombre note in a letter to Morven soon afterwards: 'In a funny sort of way, I feel I have grown up several years in a couple of weeks and that nothing can really phase me now,' he reflected. 'Life is still very full if traumatic, and if there is one lesson to be taken from Johnny's death, it is to live life to the full every day, as tomorrow might well not be there.'

Lucy had told her husband that she would not live in Kenya without him, but was so overwhelmed by the help and support from friends after her return to Nairobi that the thought of leaving never occurred to her. When it came to caring for Lucy and her two young children, Rufus and Hector, the Voorspuys and Bimb Theobald were at the front of the queue. Tristan made sure the boys were brought up to ride and enjoy the sport of polo their father had encouraged him to resume fifteen years earlier, on frequent visits to Deloraine, while Bimb taught them how to ski.

They came to regard Archie and Imo as part of their own family and Deloraine became a second home; the quartet attended pony club camps there and joined family safaris in the Mara. In the fullness of time, the boys gained a quasi-stepfather in Jamie Coulson, but it was Tristan who ensured they learnt how to carve a joint of meat, pour wine correctly and treat their fellow men and women with the same old-fashioned courtesies their mentor adhered to throughout his life.

'The way the community rallied around us after Dad died was like having a second family,' says Rufus, 'and of that core group Tristan was the one who stood out and looked after all of us without wanting a word of thanks or recognition. He made sure we did everything my father would have wanted us to do, but he kept us in line, too – he got the balance just right. He was naturally thoughtful and had this emotional intelligence of being able to gauge if I was doing something for the right or wrong reason. He was always there for us and was like a father to me and Hector.'

There are few other countries in the world where the Voorspuys' gilded and extraordinary lifestyle amongst so many close friends could possibly have been sustained from the proceeds of running a safari business. Even so, the cost of educating two children at an English public school, frequent flights abroad, keeping numerous horses, employing a huge staff and continuous entertainment was considerable, and dependent on a steady stream of Offbeat Safari bookings. Business boomed during the post *Out of Africa* years, but there was a marked downturn following the 2001 acts of terrorism in New York. 'Business is looking a bit thin for February and March at this stage, which is a bit of a blow,' Tristan wrote to Rufus a year after 9/11. 'However, bookings can come in at the last minute, so who knows?'

Tristan sometimes compared Deloraine to the monster that had to be fed, or to a ball and chain around his neck, yet his lifestyle and achievements were the envy of his friends; one of whom wrote, 'he was admired for being very much his own man, a fearless adventurer, who pursued his dream in Africa. Where we plodded, he pranced.' But Tristan worried he had not put enough by for retirement and questioned a hedonistic life of adventure with Deloraine at its centre.

'All I know is that we live an expensive lifestyle and it's hard to know where to stop,' he confided to Rufus. 'We feed roughly sixty horses and employ sixty staff, all of which have to keep going when there are no safaris.' Cindy remembers that it was difficult to pin her husband down and discuss the way forward when finances were tight. 'I had to do a lot by intuition,' she says, 'sometimes it got muddled and complicated and we were thinking on different levels. He could be a hard taskmaster.'

However worried Tristan may have been about the upkeep of Deloraine and an expensive lifestyle, he never aired his concerns publicly, compromised standards, or stinted on hospitality, deriving as much pleasure from guests' appreciation of Deloraine as their enjoyment on safari. Financial concerns were mostly short-lived, saved by the arrival of a lucrative safari booking, or perhaps banished by the intoxicating cocktail of clean air, bright sunshine, physical beauty and adventure that Africa offered. 'Somehow everything always just seemed to fall into place,' Cindy remembers.

At breakfast on the veranda, overlooking lawns shimmering with early morning dew and foliage humming with tropical birdsong, Tristan liked to point out that Deloraine could expect more than three hundred days of sunshine each year. But Deloraine is so much more than a sunny paradise on the equator; it is the only home his children have ever known, a place where they were taught to walk, swim, ride and fly; a rock around which business and family life revolved, and in their darkest times to come, Deloraine was the home that bound Tristan and Cindy together like glue.

* CHAPTER THIRTEEN *

Paradise Found

ACCORDING to the Voorspuys' close friend, Lucy Camm, Tristan was a romantic at heart who strove for a better and more fulfilling life in Africa than the outwardly hedonistic lifestyle encapsulated by parties, polo, hunting and safaris might suggest. 'We shared a love and passion of wanting to better the world,' she reflected. 'Tristan had a wish to save a piece of Africa from the effects of sprawling humanity and bring his clients' attention to its beauty and nature. He saw the revenue from wildlife tourism as an important means for protecting wildlife habitat, and helping pastoralists' needs through education in health, family planning and improved livestock husbandry.'

Tristan first explored this concept in 1995 by attempting to forge an agreement between Offbeat Safaris, KWS, and the communal owners of the Ol Kinyei Group Ranch, one of several community-owned ranches that accepted payment from Offbeat Safaris in exchange for being allowed to use their land for tourism. Group ranches had been introduced by the Kenyan government in 1968, following the 1965 Lawrence Report into land consolidation and registration, which concluded that communal registration of pastoral land was more beneficial to the inhabitants than individual ownership.

Managed by group ranch committees, they were intended to encourage investment in improvements that would increase productivity, while avoiding environmental degradation through overstocking; they also anticipated modernisation alongside traditional livestock husbandry, and the avoidance of landlessness among pastoralists. Unfortunately, these group ranch committees often failed to function effectively and, ultimately, government intervention allowed a return to subdivision, which again threatened the wildlife and habitat Tristan sought to preserve.

Offbeat's campsite at Olare Lamun lay within the Ol Kinyei Group Ranch, and unlike other community-owned lands that Tristan rode across, the owners had only agreed access with one other tourist operator. Tristan had seen fever trees destroyed by charcoal burners on the Maji Moto Group Ranch, where his rides once began, and looked on in dismay as the plough transformed the Mara's rolling eastern plains into an arable prairie unfit for wildlife.

He wanted to prevent further encroachment of the pristine Mara environment, but the pragmatist within understood this could only be achieved by demonstrating to its owners that wildlife was a valuable resource able to compete financially with other commercial uses of their land. But unlike arable farming, consumptive use of wildlife for food and tourism would also allow a traditional pastoral lifestyle to continue.

With this in mind, Tristan recruited a Kenyan friend and former officer from the British Army called Willy Knocker to assist with a project that was essentially an early forerunner of the conservancy model that in the fullness of time was to proliferate throughout Kenya. Willy set up base at the Olare Lamun campsite, surrounded by short grasslands on the western edge of the Loita Plains, where the 195,000-acre group ranch provided valuable grazing during the rainy season for plains game that does not migrate across the Mara River to the Serengeti. Ol Kinyei's wildlife credentials were further underlined by close proximity to the 938-square-mile protected wildlife sanctuary that is the Masai Mara National Reserve.

Willy's remit was to liaise with the Ol Kinyei Group Ranch committee to establish an agreement that would maximise their revenue in exchange for an undertaking to preserve habitat and wildlife. This involved drawing up a game management plan between Offbeat Safaris and the community for submission to the Kenya Wildlife Service for approval; the plan projected shared income from both tourism and the selective culling of wild game for human consumption. Although hunting had been banned since 1977, companies such as Lewa Downs, Soysambu and Game Ranching Ltd., in the Athi Plains of the Machakos District, were licensed to supply wild game to the meat trade and Nairobi restaurants such as the Carnivore, which specialised in serving exotic game.

Any game management plan lacked credibility without a wildlife count to substantiate its proposals, and government quotas for the controlled culling of surplus game would depend on the resources available. In August 1995, drivers and spotters completed this important task using six four-wheel-drive vehicles on the ground, and Tristan's Cessna for an aerial count above the most inaccessible areas. Thick scrub prevented a completely accurate assessment and concealed animals such as bush buck and water buck that favour dense cover, but during the course of three days, 18,228 Thomson's gazelle, 3,826 Grant's gazelle, 3,900 impala, 290 zebra, 178 giraffe, 10 elephant, 13 lion and 6 cheetah were recorded.

These findings formed the basis of a game management plan that was submitted to KWS the following year, but Tristan's efforts to secure a sustainable future for the Ol Kinyei Group Ranch were ultimately frustrated by the difficulties of liaising with so many individuals, and the government's decision to prohibit the consumptive utilisation of wildlife.

Willy left the project at the end of 1996, but remembers Tristan's interest in community conservation and the close relationship he enjoyed with the Maasai people across whose land he rode. 'To this day,' he recalls, 'Tristan is held in high esteem by Maasai people from the Narok district, who appreciated the revenue he brought into their communities.'

Tristan may have been diverted from the complexities and frustrations of trying to implement a conservation agreement on community-owned land by a fresh opportunity, offering him the chance to transform an overgrazed and dilapidated ranch into a sanctuary for wildlife. The suggestion came from Martin Evans, who owns and farms Ol Maisor, a 30,000-acre property in the Laikipia District of northern Kenya. Martin had arrived there with his parents and four siblings in 1968 when thirteen years old, after his family sold their land in the Rift Valley to build a new farming enterprise in the north. Their three-hundred-odd cattle and horses went by train as far as Thomson's Falls and were then driven to Ol Maisor by Martin and his brothers on horseback down an old stock route through Rumuruti Forest.

Under the leadership of their patriarch, Japper Evans, whom Tristan described as 'a stick of biltong and nearly as indestructible', the family established a successful cattle ranching enterprise with miles of stock-proof fencing. The nearest telephone for ordering fuel and provisions was at Rumuruti Post Office sixteen miles away at the end of a murram dirt track. Rumuruti was also home to the same social club that Tristan had visited to play tennis and drink beer when staying at Mutara with family friend, Tom Bower, during his first trip to Africa in 1974.

Tristan and Martin Evans were the same age, and had become friends after the Voorspuys moved to Deloraine, since his wife's family owned a trucking business in nearby Rongai. Martin and Nessie were frequently invited to join Tristan and Cindy for dinner and had often met and enjoyed the company of their safari clients.

Martin contacted Tristan in early 1999 with the news that the bank had foreclosed on a loan taken out by the former Kikuyu owner of a property bordering Ol Maisor called Sosian. The 24,000-acre ranch was in a sorry state, being in the grips of a savage drought and overrun by Samburu squatters, who had moved in to help themselves to what little grazing was left on a property that was neither farmed nor occupied by its owner.

Martin was anxious to secure a good neighbour and saw Tristan as someone well connected and passionate about conservation; even if his friend was not interested, Martin surmised, he would probably know someone who was. Sosian is less than an hour away from Deloraine by plane, and in March 1999, Tristan flew up to Laikipia for a closer inspection. He stayed overnight with the Evans family at Ol Maisor, where jacaranda trees beside the homestead shade ancient cartwheels, bleached bones of long-dead animals, and all the paraphernalia of a busy working ranch.

The next day the two men flew over Sosian, which in Samburu tongue means wild date palm, for an aerial assessment from Tristan's Cessna 182. The plane skimmed over a sunburnt land, chased by a fluttering black shadow that dipped in and out of steep rocky gorges and raced across the scrubby plains between. In years to come, a low-level flight across Sosian would startle streams of fleeing game, but in March 1999, nothing wild stirred amongst the whistling thorns and barren mellifera thickets, only herds of defeated cattle and their Samburu owners.

Tristan flew south to follow the Ewaso Narok River, trickling between hot rocks from one oversized puddle to the next, and spotted the pale froth of shrunken falls that would normally thunder thirty tumultuous feet into the pool below. Tall fever trees marked the river's passage through Sosian like a green stripe across the corner of an ochre canvas, and empty dams simmered like scabs in the heat. The land was speckled in clean white bones, disparate Samburu bomas, and red tracks their tenants had worn through the bush.

Where some would have seen only death and despair, Tristan saw the rugged grandeur of a spectacular landscape, and the certainty of life-sustaining rain. He had lived in Africa long enough to understand the terrible but transient nature of a drought, and knew that when rain returned to Sosian, the wildlife would follow.

Although some of Laikipia County's two million acres have been subdivided and lost forever to wildlife, the sprawling landscape of rocks, scrub, rivers and woodland is still home to many of Kenya's largest privately owned estates. Once the preserve of indigenous Laikipia Maasai, the region has undergone dramatic social changes since being designated part of the Northern Maasai Reserve by British colonial rule in 1904. This arrangement was abandoned after only seven years, and a new agreement made with the Maasai elders for their people to move south into fertile lands straddling the borders of Kenya and Tanzania.

The move was completed by 1913, and after the First World War large tracts of Laikipia were settled by Europeans, some of whom immigrated under the British Government's soldier settler scheme.[39] Elsewhere, a vacuum left by the departed Maasai was quickly filled by their traditional Samburu enemies from the north, and by Kikuyu people moving up from the south. Laikipia is now home to a diverse mix of tribes including Kikuyu, Samburu, Maasai, Turkana and Pokot.

Early European settlers discovered that much of the poor-quality land in the northern and eastern parts of the district were unsuitable for cultivation, but extensive, low-impact ranching allowed the indigenous wildlife to prosper. Laikipia is home to endemic species such as the Jackson's hartebeest, reticulated giraffe, and Grevy's zebra, along with healthy populations of other plains game and all of the African Big Five,

---

39 The placing of ex-service men on foreign land was a widespread response by the governments of the British Empire to the problems of reconstruction after the First World War.

although the few remaining rhino are now guarded round the clock by armed rangers. Wild dogs had been exterminated by overzealous ranchers in the early twentieth century, but in 1999 were poised to make a successful return to the region.

Tristan had spent much time in Laikipia since his first visit to Mutara and become firm friends with many farmers and conservationists there. He had met several of the region's tough ranching characters such as Gilfrid Powys from Suyian, and admired the stunning Laragai House that his friend, Valentine Cecil, had built on the Dyers' Borana Ranch[40] nearby. Tristan had ridden across large tracts of Laikipia, too, a few years earlier, recording that he had seen four hundred eland and several hundred zebra on a long, hot ride from Kisima to Il Pinguin.

Tristan returned to Deloraine fired up by his first visit to Sosian, which Martin had temporarily secured by signing a sales agreement and paying a deposit raised amongst friends. Removing the ranch from the open market gave Tristan valuable breathing space, but the bank was asking the equivalent of £30 an acre, which when added to the cost of kick-starting Sosian, amounted to a million pounds sterling.

As he could not possibly find such a large sum alone, Tristan resolved to form a consortium of like-minded individuals to secure the threatened ranch for wildlife conservation. He applied characteristic enthusiasm and energy to the project, contacting anyone he thought might be suitable and interested in joining his scheme.

He approached Petre Barclay's son, Jonti, who like Tristan, had served with the Blues and Royals in the British Army and become a close family friend. 'Tristan worked on the basis that you can't buy a cupboard in Kensington for a hundred grand, let alone a piece of Africa,' Jonti remembers.

When visiting Sosian, he was not deterred by the lack of fencing and wrecked buildings, or even the tick-infested sheep and goats that had taken up residence in the main house. Where others saw scorched earth and no grazing, Jonti saw an opportunity to participate in an exciting conservation

---

40 The Dyers are a farming family from Laikipia and close friends of the Voorspuys. They own Borana Lodge, a top-end tourist destination similar to Sosian.

venture. He told Tristan that he would love to be involved, and that if the 'wild and lovely land' was not secured, it would be lost forever to intensive cropping, to which Tristan replied, 'Over my dead body.'

Tristan wrote to Morven in November to solicit his interest. 'The ranch in Rumuruti is finally proceeding and the owners have asked for a sale agreement, which means we are at the deposit stage. Are you interested in a 10% share at £100,000 for 24,000 acres of Laikipia, including a three-year development plan?' he asked, before drawing attention to the practical benefits. 'After that it should be self-sustaining and your asset value could rise considerably, though there will be no dividends. Each shareholder gets the right to build a house on the property, which would be lovely for retirement and is probably my long-term plan. It's all exciting stuff, and will keep me out of mischief for some time to come.'

Morven wasn't tempted, but retired safari guide Chris Orme-Smith and his wife, Teresa, joined Jonti as shareholders, along with an American couple from California, who had recently retired to South Africa.

Richard Constant happened to join a Mara riding safari when Tristan was actively seeking investors; the Yorkshireman had considered buying land in South Africa, but was told Kenya offered much better prospects. Throughout the ride, Richard listened to his guide's plans to save Sosian from subdivision and cropping, and two weeks later flew back out to take a closer look.

'Sosian was in the grips of a drought; there were no animals, just bones on the ground,' he remembers. 'But the romantic nature of the countryside was so stunning that it was easy to imagine what it would look like after the rains came down. So I handed over the money in a leap of faith and began a close friendship that lasted for the next eighteen years.'

During that time, Richard's daughters both worked at Sosian and his house overlooking a dam there became his principal residence. Tristan's only real disagreement with Richard was over a photograph of him posing with a dead cobra. 'There is nothing at all wrong with snakes,' Tristan fumed, 'people like you just don't understand them.'

After the sale went through, staff employed by the former owner had to be paid off, and squatters given notice to leave; within a few months all the Samburu and their livestock had left. Martin Evans helped draw up a three-year plan to farm the ranch extensively and agreed to take on the day-to-day management until someone permanent could be found. One of his first jobs was to build a four-kilometre wall denoting the boundary between Sosian and an overgrazed neighbour, but elsewhere boundaries remained deliberately fenceless to allow the free movement of wildlife. The dry-stone wall took a year to complete and was constructed from rocks collected in wheelbarrows, and beaten into shape with blunt hammers.

Within a few months, a genial Afrikaner named Hannes Nel had been recruited by Jonti and Martin Evans to manage the farm; he brought his wife, Lorian, two small daughters and an assortment of dogs, some of which ended up being eaten by leopards. Hannes, who was strong, cheerful and able, started from scratch with thirty in-calf cows from Ol Maisor and quickly proved to be the perfect man to knock a run-down ranch into shape. He was also a talented builder, creating three stone houses for investors, as well as a swimming pool and exotic cabana for the use of paying guests staying at the lodge.

The manager responded to a lack of social life and demise of the legendary Rumuruti Club by building his own watering hole for the enjoyment of friends and neighbours in Laikipia. The Lugga boasted a concrete dance floor, a wooden dart board and a well-stocked bar. Hannes suspended a neon sign from the club's thatched-reed roof and opened at least one night a month; patrons played basketball by moonlight, danced to music powered by car batteries, and slept in tents pitched on the grass outside.

Back at Deloraine, Mark Laurence had been busy preparing for the start of the riding safari season with a new assistant. Jakob von Plessen had arrived from Argentina in April after the British military attaché in Buenos Aires suggested he write to Tristan asking for work. Eighteen-year-old Jakob broke in the horses at his family farm at Mar del Plata, but he was not the high-goal polo player Tristan was expecting when he met him off the plane in Nairobi. They drove to the Muthaiga Club in stony silence and took off from Wilson airport early the following morning in Tristan's plane.

Up in the air, Jakob made the mistake of telling his new boss that he had flown a little back in Argentina. 'If that's the case,' said Tristan, 'take control of the steering and keep on this bearing. Mind the volcano and wake me up in forty-five minutes.' Jakob remembers the flight as being one of the tensest experiences of his life, but woke Tristan above the airstrip at Gogar Farm as instructed. Jakob took to safari life with enthusiasm, at first 'just tagging along behind Mark Laurence pretending to be barman,' but soon becoming a real asset, and someone Cindy trusted to ride the younger, uneducated horses. 'I was quite obedient, which Tristan liked,' he recalls.

Four months later, Christl von Plessen joined her son for an Offbeat riding safari through the Mara, although she had visited Kenya many times previously and already fallen under the country's spell. Christl returned to her interior-decorating business in Argentina after the safari ended, but when she heard shares in Sosian were still available a year later, she was tempted back for a closer look. 'I always had Kenya in my mind,' she says. 'I knew there could be trouble one day, but I was never thinking for a second about business, I was just thinking of realising a dream.'

Sosian was still drought-stricken when Tristan drove Christl, her partner Michel and a Buenos Aires architect to inspect the property in February 2001. She was horrified by the desolate view after they stopped beside the boundary wall, which workers were toiling to complete beneath the ruthless sun. 'And this is Sosian,' Tristan said, indicating miles of parched land and skeletal trees. Christl said nothing, but secretly hoped for a charming homestead instead of the rusty tin shack that awaited.

Despite her disappointment, she decided to invest. 'I remembered how well Tristan organised everything on safari and the special mix of simplicity and luxury,' she says. 'I knew how much he loved Kenya and that he was not rich enough to do a completely foolish thing. I just trusted him.' Long overdue rains had transformed the landscape by the time Jakob's mother returned to Sosian in May, and the Ewaso Nyiro River was now a foaming brown torrent cascading through a land of high, green grass and leafy trees. She inspected the ranch house with other shareholders and agreed to convert the run-down property into a lodge for paying guests, but with an Argentine flavour different to the homogenous East African safari lodge. 'No one really knew me,' she says, 'but they just trusted me to get on with it.'

It took Christl and builders from Naivasha two years to complete extensive renovations, during an era when Argentine materials and furniture were uniquely cheap, following the government's devaluation of the peso. Her Argentine architect, grateful for work when there was none back home, made sweeping changes to the 'charmless and awful' abode Christl had originally been shown. During visits to supervise progress, Christl lodged with Hannes and Lorian, who were generous and amusing hosts.

'Staying with them was a constant adventure,' she remembers. 'I just loved every second of building Sosian up from zero. I was completely happy, everything was new, and it was an adventure. I am so grateful the other shareholders backed me.' When lack of finance threatened to bring renovations to a premature halt, Christl knew what had to be done; she purchased another share. She later built her own modest house on the ranch, selecting a private site surrounded by wait-a-bit thorn, and modelling the round stone building with a thatched roof on the Italian cottage at the main lodge.

It quickly became clear to the Sosian board that running the ranch was going to cost much more than anyone had anticipated – and there was still one unallocated share waiting to be taken up. Anthony Deal was a successful property investor from the UK, who had first met Tristan on a riding safari in October 1997. By the time Anthony and his wife, Fiona, returned for a second safari four years later, their eldest son had completed a stint working for Offbeat during gardening leave from Kleinwort Benson. Anthony and Fiona visited the unfinished lodge at Sosian after their ride ended, and were briefed on various projects running out of control. But within twenty-four hours they were in, and the last remaining share in Sosian had been sold.

CHAPTER FOURTEEN

Of Elephants and Men

SIX months before his death, in a written response to an enquiry regarding his inclusion in a list of leading safari guides in Kenya, Tristan confirmed that elephants were 'very easily' his favourite animal. On safari, in prose and in conversation, he frequently drew parallels between the giant pachyderms and mankind, pointing out that elephants and humanity have similar life spans, attain puberty at the same age and are both family orientated. Tristan loved watching elephants going about their everyday business, was impressed by their intelligence and fascinated by their diverse range of vocabulary, but he sometimes let his enthusiasm get the better of him on safari.

His diaries bear testament to the fact he was often charged by disgruntled elephants, having got too close to them on horseback, much to the alarm of clients that had to sit tight when their mounts whipped around and fled. Even the most determined elephants were no match for thoroughbred horses, who quickly opened up a significant lead on their pursuers in what Tristan regarded as a harmless game. Mock or otherwise, most charges were by female elephants, whom he admired for their bravery and 'attractive human-like breasts'.

The maudlin in him reflected that both species can overpopulate and destroy their own environment, but that elephants come a poor second to man in that respect. Most of all, he deplored their suffering at the hands of man simply for the crime of wearing ivory, and believed elephants worthy of our sympathy, respite and respect. 'Man's overpopulation of the planet is very much threatening their long-term survival,' he wrote in 2016, 'and extinction in their natural environment is possible this century.'

Back in 2000, while accompanying his neighbour, Hamish Grant, on a trip to Harare to collect a new plane, Tristan suggested they make a detour to Braeside, near the renamed Zimbabwean town of Chinhoyi, where his old friend, Rory Hensman, was making a name for himself through his pioneering work with elephants. Twelve years earlier, Rory had hand-reared two orphaned elephant calves, and was struck by their intelligence and willingness to please.

This led to him teaching them, and others that followed, to assist with tasks on the farm such as herding cattle, checking fence lines, and tracking a human scent, which they accomplished so efficiently that Rory considered deploying them on anti-poaching patrols to the Zambezi Valley, where large numbers of elephant and rhino were being slaughtered by poachers.

To the uninitiated, using elephants to track down poachers may seem implausible; apart from anything else, a six-ton elephant presents an easy target for anyone carrying an AK-47 assault rifle. However, after being chased through the Zambezi bushland for two kilometres by a cow elephant, Rory surmised that when combined with the ability to cross rivers, move quietly by night or day, and survive off the bush, the elephants' refined tracking abilities would make it an effective instrument in the war against poaching. They could also be trained to halt pursuit when they got within a few hundred yards of their human quarry, at which point armed handlers could dismount from their high vantage points and approach the criminals on foot.

Rory was frustrated by politics and Robert Mugabe's brutal regime from attaining his dream of using domesticated elephants to protect their wild brethren in the national parks alongside the Zambezi River, but in 1993 one of his elephants successfully tracked down a robber who had broken into a neighbouring farmhouse.

Rory was called in after police dogs had been unable to follow the thief's scent through a field of smelly paprika, but a fifteen-year-old male elephant called Somapane picked up the trail without difficulty and followed it for several kilometres, crossing the Hunyani River four times and passing through the middle of a huge farming compound that was home to thousands of African workers. The trail ended at the robber's home, where the police found his shoes on the veranda and a stash of stolen property inside the house. The miscreant was arrested later the same day.

Instead of fighting crime, the Hensman's growing herd of domesticated elephants became ambassadors for the plight of their wild cousins through tourism and conservation initiatives. Some were sent up to Victoria Falls to carry paying clients on elephant back safaris, but more remained on the Hensman's farm at Braeside. Tristan and Hamish's stay there coincided with a visit from the Zimbabwe minister of tourism, Francis Nema, who had been invited to observe the benefits of elephants to tourism first hand.

Rory laid on a memorable display for his guests, first taking them to a cattle dip, where three elephants under the instruction of a single mounted handler proceeded to herd cattle into the dip, slipping their trunks beneath the bellies of the most recalcitrant and shuffling them forwards on two legs, or prodding them gently into the dip with long white tusks, just as they would with their own young.

The elephants were next shown a group of six farm workers sitting beneath a tree, who were each dressed in a different colour. Half an hour after the men were asked to run off and hide, the red hat one of them had been wearing was shown to an elephant, which at once set off in pursuit, travelling at a fast walk while the spectators followed in Rory's blue Land Rover. To their astonishment, the elephant located the man dressed in red after following his scent for more than four kilometres through the bush.

After lunch, Hamish and Tristan were submerged to their waists in warm water as they rode the huge beasts across the same dam where Tristan was nearly killed in a speedboat accident in 1982. Rory recounted how half a dozen elephants had once stopped swimming to turn around in unison and stare with open ears into the distance. Three kilometres away in the direction of their gaze, and at exactly the same time, a friend had wrecked her car in a crash that the animal's handlers could neither see nor hear.

Tristan, who had been toying with the idea of training elephants in Kenya for the last few years, was much impressed by what he had seen at Braeside. He had written to the esteemed Kenya-born elephant guru, the late Daphne Sheldrick, in 1997 to solicit her views on elephant back safaris, and held up Rory Hensman as an example of an elephant trainer, whose charges were 'showered with love and affection and very happy.'

Daphne was a respected and successful rehabilitator of elephants, who had created the David Sheldrick Wildlife Trust (DSWT) after the death of her husband in 1977, and was later awarded an MBE in recognition of her pioneering work. The DSWT operates the most successful orphan elephant rescue-and-rehabilitation programme in the world, and is one of the pioneering conservation organisations for wildlife and habitat protection in East Africa.

For all of these reasons, Tristan's ambitions to bring domesticated elephants to Kenya could never come to fruition without Daphne Sheldrick's support. She wrote a gracious reply to his letter, but made no secret of her dislike of and suspicion towards any kind of elephant training or commercialisation, citing as an example the sorry plight of an elephant named Dunda, who had been unforgivably abused in the San Diego Zoo.

'If this can happen in a reputable institution such as San Diego, perpetrated by an acknowledged "elephant expert",' she wrote, 'how can you ensure that the same will not be repeated elsewhere, bearing in mind not every operator will be as caring of elephants as you.' She believed that one must consider 'the long-term repercussions of creating such a precedence, and take a hard look at the abuse of donkeys and other beasts of burden in Africa to realise that compassion and kindness are rare commodities.'

It was clear Mrs Sheldrick was unlikely to compromise her strongly held beliefs on elephant commercialisation, although her own organisation received significant revenues from tourism. Tristan responded by agreeing to disagree, writing, 'One part of me says I should follow your instincts and leave the whole thing well alone. Another says we have caused so much suffering to elephants and our lives are so inextricably linked anyway that there maybe is good cause for trying to learn more by intimate contact.'

Tristan remained as polite in his prose to Daphne as she had been to him, but concluded that commercialisation of wildlife does not necessarily lead to corruption. 'I run a commercial operation in order to live,' he pointed out, 'but believe I put more into wildlife conservation than I take out.'

While Tristan's efforts were unsuccessful, his love and respect for elephants remained undiminished. When asked to nominate his most memorable wildlife sighting after a lifetime of observation, Tristan chose a profoundly moving encounter with elephants ahead of numerous other extraordinary natural history experiences.

'I have seen many kills by large predators which are fascinating,' he wrote, 'but my most lasting memory is of a family of twenty or so elephant frolicking and bathing in the Rofwero River in Meru National Park in around 1986, when the population there was plummeting through poaching, and they were always frightened and running away from vehicles. They swam and splashed for half an hour or more, as if to say there may be no tomorrow. It was a tear-making experience.'

It is almost certain the elephants that moved Tristan to tears that day are no longer alive; between 1980 and 1990 the elephant population in Meru plunged from a healthy two thousand head to just two hundred and fifty restless, hunted and traumatised individuals.

Soon after Tristan's visit to Braeside, the Hensman's farm was invaded by Robert Mugabe's war veterans, which for Rory signalled the beginning of the end of normal life. The elephants were bizarrely accused of being used for psychological warfare and faced certain death unless they were moved to safety. Their predicament precipitated another flurry of activity from Tristan, who recognised the elephants' plight as a way of securing a safe future for the Hensman family and some of their elephants in East Africa.

He wrote to the KWS chairman, Richard Leakey, in August 2002, enclosing a draft proposal for bringing the Hensman's elephants to Sosian, where he hoped they could be the forerunners of an elephant safari business that Tristan was convinced would benefit both tourism and wildlife. He included a potted history of Offbeat Safaris and Randall Moore's successful elephant back safaris in Botswana, a brief synopsis of tourism in Kenya, and a detailed description of Laikipia that included a carefully considered sample itinerary for elephant safaris at Sosian.

In the same letter, Tristan also took the opportunity of registering his objection to the manner in which the KWS and Mrs Sheldrick's elephant orphanage in Nairobi had dealt with an orphaned elephant that Hannes Nel and Martin Evans had recently rescued at Sosian. The three-year-old elephant was secured for his own safety by a sisal rope attached to one hind leg, and had settled down so quickly in his stable at Sosian that he was soon eating titbits from the hands of the man assigned to look after him. Tristan telephoned the KWS's elephant expert, Patrick Omondi, at the organisation's headquarters in Nairobi to inform him, and during the conversation suggested that since the elephant was already weaned, he might be allowed to remain at Sosian.

Despite having asked to be kept updated, Tristan did not hear back from anyone at KWS, but the following day Hannes was told that an aircraft would be arriving at Rumuruti to remove the young elephant to the orphanage in accordance with KWS policy. Several days after the elephant had been taken away 'without a word of thanks or encouragement', Tristan called into to its new home to check up on progress and remonstrate with Mrs Sheldrick over the way the whole affair had been handled, but was taken aback when she accused him of cruelty and having kept the rescue secret for several days.

'Nothing could be further from the truth,' Tristan protested, 'and it was even more galling to learn that tourist visitors to the orphanage were being told the latest addition had been captured on a ranch and held for several days hobbled by people trying to keep the elephant and not tell KWS.'

The goalposts had moved since Tristan's initial efforts to keep and train domesticated elephants had been rebuffed by Mrs Sheldrick; this time the lives of Rory's Zimbabwe elephants were under threat, and he now had 24,000 acres of Laikipia in which to accommodate them. Richard Leakey referred Tristan to Dr Paula Kanumbu, whose early conservation work had been to measure Kenya's ivory stockpile prior to incineration in 1989; she had since joined KWS and become a passionate advocate against the renewal of the international trade in ivory. Tristan wrote to her, offering to fly up to five board members of the KWS to see Rory Hensman's elephants at his own expense, but the familiarisation trip never materialised, and he eventually and reluctantly had to admit a rare and dispiriting defeat.

The Hensmans' twelve remaining elephants were transported to South Africa in a convoy of lorries, arriving at their new home after an exhausting twenty-hour journey, but they were safely away from Zimbabwe, where poachers ran amok across once-peaceful game farms indiscriminately slaughtering the wildlife. Forced to abandon a productive farm that had been cut out of uninhabited bush nearly a century earlier, the Hensmans' problems were far from over.

Rory's beloved elephants remained at their new home, but after several frustrating months, Rory saw no option other than to walk away and start up once more on his own. In 2003, he formed 'Elephants for Africa Forever', near the remote town of Tzaneen, to re-home problem elephants, starting with a rogue male called Tembo, who had caused a million Rand's worth of damage after a male rival eloped with his female companion. His trail of destruction included the killing of a rhino and buffalo, breaking into buildings, and upturning vehicles. 'He was not wanted at all,' Rory's son, Sean, remembers, 'a bit like we were feeling at the time.'

In 2010, Rory moved 450 kilometres south and established 'Adventures with Elephants' at Bela Bela, north of Johannesburg, which became the headquarters of the Rory Hensman Conservation and Research Unit. Founded in 2016, the unit focuses on all aspects of elephant research and welfare, and strives to deliver workable solutions to a variety of wildlife challenges. Rory is no longer with us, but his legacy endures through his son Sean, who spent several months working for Tristan as a young man and retains fond memories of the close and 'passionate' family friend whom he first met as an infant at Braeside.

Now completely cured of any aggressive tendencies, the Hensmans' flagship elephant weighs six tons and stands three and a half metres tall. 'Tembo is the kindest, gentlest elephant you could ever hope to meet,' says Sean. 'All he needed was attention; I would happily place a two-year-old child at his feet.'

* CHAPTER FIFTEEN *

Expanding Horizons

TRISTAN and Cindy had first ridden across Laikipia on an exploratory ride soon after they were married, where access across land that belonged to close friends was easier than liaising with group ranch committees in the Mara. The purchase of Sosian provided Offbeat Safaris with a northern base, and ready access to countless square miles of diverse and beautiful scenery, offering quality game viewing. Laikipia could never rival the Mara for the sheer numbers of plains game that swarm across her grassy plains during the migration, but the wilder and privately owned plateau offers a varied landscape of secluded river valleys, sweeping escarpments, plunging rocky gorges, and sprawling thickets of dense scrub.

Tristan appreciated the differences between the two regions and saw the potential of adding a northern riding itinerary across Laikipia to complement Offbeat's well-established rides in the Mara. He hoped these would be an attractive option for repeat guests hooked on the Offbeat experience, but eager to explore a different region of Kenya on horseback.

Offbeat started offering regular set departure rides[41] from Sosian long before renovations to the lodge had been completed, and with the land green following heavy rain, the expeditions were an instant success. These mobile rides started at a secluded location beside the Ewaso Narok River that became known as Tristan's Camp, and finished many miles later amongst elephants and tall cedar trees, seven thousand feet high in the stunning Lolldaiga Hills. Mount Kenya, the second-highest mountain in Africa, provides a constant backdrop to the ride; her summit at just over

---

41 Rides where the dates are pre-published and guaranteed to run, as opposed to tailor-made rides for a specific group of friends or family.

17,000 feet can only be seen from Sosian in the clearest early morning light, but is so close by the end of the ride that guests can discern snowdrifts beneath her jagged peaks.

Some clients reach Sosian by road from Deloraine or Nairobi, passing through Nakuru, Thomson's Falls and Rumuruti during a five-hour drive through African villages, farmland and bush. Others fly direct to the lodge's dirt airstrip by private charter, or on a scheduled flight to the northern hub of Nanyuki, an hour's drive from Sosian. During the northern ride, guests traverse private ranches, where conservation takes precedence over commercial farming and most of the fences have been taken down to allow free movement of wildlife.

Riding across remote properties such as Loisaba and Mpala, which each run to sixty thousand acres, feels like a true wilderness experience for clients used to a Mara landscape shared with pastoralists and their ubiquitous herds of livestock. Laikipian farming families are sometimes invited to join clients for lunch or dinner when the ride passes through their properties, and the opportunity to learn of their history and lifestyle first-hand adds another popular dimension to the experience.

As Offbeat Safaris continued to grow, clients were sometimes offered the chance to extend their holiday after the ride had ended by visiting other attractions within Kenya, as a forerunner to what would become a complete safari service, where transfers, domestic flights and any destination in the country could be booked and paid for through Offbeat.

Sosian was a convenient launch pad into the arid northern deserts, and a flying visit to the Chalbi Desert and Lake Turkana became a popular extension for those interested in visiting a remarkable landscape where little has changed in centuries. Guests stayed in reed-thatched cottages at the tiny Kalacha Camp, overlooking a palm-lined oasis on the northern edge of the Chalbi Desert, where members of the nomadic Gabbra tribe appear with their camels every morning to collect fresh water.

The springs also attract large flocks of sandgrouse, which flight in to drink soon after dawn and, until the Kenyan government's ban on bird shooting, were a legitimate and delicious quarry species. Tristan incorporated bird shoots into the Chalbi extension, and took Archie along whenever possible to help gather the bag for breakfast. Each gun was limited to twenty birds, and shooting was prohibited during the breeding season, when males carry droplets of water on their breast feathers back to their thirsty chicks. But weather patterns around which the seasons were based are often unpredictable in dry equatorial lands, and Tristan would abandon the shoot if any grouse were picked up with damp breast feathers.

Tristan flew in and out of the sun-baked sands surrounding Kalacha on numerous occasions, occasionally colliding with one of the acacias lining the path along which a pilot must taxi to and from the airstrip. Jonti Barclay once watched in astonishment from the cockpit of his own plane as Tristan, who was bumping along the track in front of him, struck a branch, disembarked and wrapped duct tape around the gaping hole in the wing, before getting back in and executing a perfect take-off.

A stay at Kalacha Camp also included a flying visit to Lake Turkana's South Island at the black centre of the Rift Valley, where the bleak airstrip is precariously short, but devoid of any trees. The lake held a special place in Tristan's affections, for he had visited her rocky shores during his first African safari with Morven in 1974, and had been heartened to recognise the familiar, dark-green sheen of the Jade Sea, when flying into Kenya with Roland Purcell at the end of their epic flight from England twenty years later.

He enjoyed introducing clients and friends to the harsh, volcanic landscape that is often compared to the surface of the moon, and showing them how to catch huge Nile perch with rods stowed away at the back of his plane. Having caught lunch, Tristan would take off again for Loiyangalani on the south-eastern shores of the lake, often detouring to fly over El Molo Bay, which is home to the eponymous endemic tribe, before landing close to the Oasis Hotel as casually as tourists might drive between sights within a city. Loiyangalani was then a small and nondescript town of little more than a thousand inhabitants, but has become better known since being chosen as a location for *The Constant Gardener*.

The Offbeat portfolio of riding safaris was further extended in 2004 by an exploratory safari through Amboseli, in conjunction with the UK-based travel company, Wild & Exotic, which began close to the Tanzanian border town of Namanga and traversed the dried-up bed of Lake Amboseli, before ending with a day tracking rare black rhino across lava flows in the Chyulu Hills ninety miles to the east.

Offbeat had previously collaborated with Wild & Exotic on one-off riding itineraries, including an ascent of Mount Kenya on horseback as far as the Rutundu log cabins close to Lake Alice, at an altitude of 10,200 feet. Different again from either the Mara or Laikipia, the Amboseli ride promised long, trouble-free gallops, interaction with large herds of elephant, and impressive views of Africa's highest mountain. But it was also a dry and arid region, which meant that sufficient water to last the whole ride had to be transported from camp to camp in a large bowser tank.

The first ride was so successful that Amboseli joined the Offbeat Safaris riding portfolio, offering clients the chance to explore a third, very different region of Kenya on horseback. 'The country is spectacular with Mt Kilimanjaro as a backdrop and the Chyulu Hills are the final destination,' Tristan wrote to his mother-in-law after completing his second ride there. 'The lake bed of Amboseli stretches for miles and is soft underfoot with hardly any holes and the best going for horses that we operate in by far. We rode for a week without seeing another white man and relatively few Maasai. Now we know what we are doing, I hope to ride there more often.'

Tristan appreciated the Amboseli terrain as being ideal for horses, but the region was no better than the Mara when it came to harbouring the dreaded tsetse fly, whose bite can infect the victim with trypanosomiasis. Also known as sleeping sickness or TRIPs, the disease has an incubation period of up to eight weeks, attacks the central nervous system, and is frequently fatal. African horse sickness is an equally nasty illness spread by biting midges, ticks and other insects. Offbeat horses were inoculated at the beginning of every safari season, but over the years many more succumbed to these pernicious infections than were ever lost to lion.

By 2005, concerns following the terrorist attacks on New York four years earlier were fading, and American tourists were returning to Kenya in droves; in the same letter, Tristan expressed concern that he had 'over committed' to safari bookings during a frantic dry season schedule. 'I am flat out from July to September non-stop on six consecutive safaris, which

I have never done before,' he explained. 'So much will be going on it is ridiculous, and although Archie might come on the odd safari with me, I feel guilty that I will be spending so little time with my family during the summer holidays.'

Luckily there was a permanent queue of young men and women volunteering to help Offbeat out during their gap year between school and university; they anticipated exciting safari adventures, but parents who knew Tristan personally saw an opportunity for their children to be taught the skills of self-reliance, responsibility, and consideration for others that he instilled in everyone who worked for him. 'The parents of half of the wet-behind-the-ears public schoolboys in England should be grateful for the way Tristan and Cindy shepherded their kids,' is how Julieta Keene put it after her own two-year placement with the Voorspuys.

Some of the Offbeat helpers, such as Jakob von Plessen and Julieta, stayed for years rather than months, although Julieta had already left by the time Piers Winkworth arrived in June 2002. Well-connected and financially secure, twenty-five-year-old Piers had quit his job in the city a year earlier to work at his father's racing stables in Surrey, where the assistant trainer was an old friend of Mark Laurence's. Keen for some adventure in his life, Piers followed up on the introduction and began an association with Offbeat Safaris that would ultimately complete the company's expansion from being a provider of single-destination riding safaris to a full-blown safari operator.

Piers's relationship with Offbeat got off to an inauspicious start on his first safari, when his horse put its foot in an aardvark hole and catapulted him over his head in a crashing fall. After everyone had pulled up, Tristan trotted back to the rookie assistant and castigated him for falling off. 'You told me you'd been riding racehorses all your life,' he fumed, 'Offbeat guides are not allowed to fall off, it's only clients that can do that,' but Tristan calmed down when he realised the extent of Piers's injuries. Fortunately for Piers there was an American nurse on the ride, who being a veteran of many previous Offbeat safaris was quite unafraid of Tristan. She insisted that Piers be taken to hospital in Nanyuki, where it took more than thirty stitches to secure his dangling ear back in place.

Jakob von Plessen was busy pioneering his own rides through Patagonia when Piers started with Offbeat, but Jakob's return from Argentina two years later to resume guiding duties for Tristan may have been the catalyst for some seismic changes amongst senior Offbeat staff. Mark Laurence had been a dependable and effective mainstay since joining Offbeat twelve years earlier and remembers Tristan as being 'a man of few words, extremely kind, a bad temper,' who taught him manners and respect for others.

'He wanted you to succeed, but there was no pampering,' Mark says. 'You had to sort things out for yourself.' When Mark wanted to buy a Land Cruiser, he asked Tristan if he could borrow a large sum of money to secure the vehicle. 'Why come to me for a fucking loan?' Tristan asked before storming off, but the next day he overcame his aversion to Japanese vehicles and, without ceremony or paperwork, handed over twelve thousand US dollars, which he then helped Mark to repay by hiring the vehicle back for use on safaris.

Just as Tristan had done before him, Mark Laurence started to accumulate his own safari equipment with a view to one day setting up on his own. Mark was doing a job he loved for a man he respected as a father-figure, while being paid handsomely for the privilege. He was a hit with the clients, too, one guest describing him as 'a remarkable and professional guide with an uncanny sixth sense about animals.'

Mark had seen enough of Cindy's hard work behind the scenes at Deloraine to appreciate the complexities of owning and running a safari business, compared to the carefree existence of a well-paid guide, but when he was introduced to a wealthy potential backer, the temptation to go it alone was too great to resist. The pragmatist in Tristan recognised his assistant's departure had only been a matter of time, and he made no effort to dissuade him from leaving.

However, Tristan did have something to say when he realised Jakob was also considering jumping ship to join Mark, in a venture that promised better camping facilities and luxurious touches such as chandeliers in the mess tent. Jakob also regarded Tristan as something of a father-figure, describing him as his 'hero and mentor'. Like almost everyone who worked for Tristan, Jakob was 'terrified' of disappointing him and remembers dreading having to contact his boss by satellite telephone to explain why he had shot a charging hippo on safari. When Tristan came on the line, Jakob took a deep breath and recounted every detail of what had taken place. 'I was expecting a monumental bollocking,' he remembers, 'but Tristan just told me to drag the hippo away from camp, slit it open and you will have a big feast of lion and hyena. That was not the response I expected, but I was hugely relieved.'

It was rare for Tristan to intervene in the lives of anyone who worked for him, so when the man of few words opened up to offer serious advice, as he did to Jakob at the time of Mark's departure, the beneficiary tended to sit up and take notice. He invited Jakob to accompany him for a walk through the gardens at Deloraine after breakfast, during which he warned Jakob about the pitfalls of joining Mark in a venture sponsored by dubious South African backers.

Tristan ended by giving the Argentine a big hug and admitting he would hate to lose him also from the Offbeat team. 'There aren't many of us in this tribe,' he smiled, referring to the small collection of people he regarded as qualified to guide a riding safari through the African bush, 'but you are one of them.' Tristan's advice that morning secured the services of Jakob for many years to come.

Jakob was the ideal person to guide riding safaris, but if Tristan identified a lack of direction in any of his assistants, he felt obliged to highlight the drawbacks of a carefree African existence. Two years after Piers Winkworth's arrival in Africa, Tristan told him it was time to find his own standing within Kenya and move on from the fun but undemanding role of assistant guide. This advice coincided with Tristan's desire to expand Offbeat's business to include a non-riding circuit of safari destinations to complement Deloraine and Sosian.

As all his riding camps in the Mara were temporary, Tristan decided Offbeat needed a permanent presence there, close to where the Olare Orok lugga flows between rolling hills, through an area that is a haven for wildlife. He was also interested in Meru, a beautiful national park more than a hundred miles to the west of Sosian, where George and Joy Adamson reared Elsa, an orphaned lion cub whose life and rehabilitation back into the wild were the subject of the award-winning 1966 film, *Born Free*.

The 540-square-mile park is divided by thirteen rivers that rise in the eastern Nyambene Hills and flow south through a varied landscape of savannah, riverine forest and swamps. Tristan had explored Meru many times and enjoyed some spectacular wildlife sightings there, but he deplored the scale of poaching that went on during the 1990s, when the elephant population plummeted by more than eighty-five per cent. However, since 2000, the KWS had been eradicating poaching and improving infrastructure in the national park, to such good effect that Tristan envisaged a camp in Meru complementing Sosian on a northern safari circuit

Tristan had already admitted to Piers that he felt responsible for allowing him to enjoy a relaxed safari life in Kenya, when he could have been pursuing a more lucrative and conventional career, and in late 2004 revealed a plan that would provide him with real responsibility and prospects. 'Tristan squared up to me and said that it was time to get serious,' Piers remembers, 'and that he had the perfect project in mind. He told me about his dream of a non-riding safari circuit through Laikipia, Meru and the Mara, and a few weeks later we flew up to Meru and had a scout around for potential campsites.'

The following June, Piers opened two semi-permanent camps near the Olare Orok lugga on the Koyiaki Group Ranch in the Mara, and at Bisanadi National Reserve, just north of Meru National Park. The Voorspuys retained a minority share in both camps, which trade under the Offbeat name, but are principally owned and run by Piers. Offbeat Mara and Offbeat Meru shared the same design of six spacious guest tents, supplied with an ensuite loo and traditional bucket shower, close to a roomy mess tent where guests can dine and relax between escorted game drives.

However sublime the location, African safari camps are only as good as their managers, who are usually drawn from a wildlife, conservation or guiding background. A Kenyan-born guide from Nanyuki was recruited to build and run Offbeat Meru, whilst Piers moved into Offbeat Mara at Olare Orok, and spent three years assimilating the challenges and rewards of managing a successful safari camp. An office shared between Offbeat riding safaris, which had been organised entirely by Cindy, and the new

Offbeat camps, was established at Nanyuki Airport, which Tristan hoped would make life a little easier for his wife. 'Cindy is always working flat out,' he wrote in a letter to her mother, 'though we now have the new Nanyuki office hopefully taking the strain on bookings. To be fair it is very hard for us both to be in the same office.'

Tristan's optimism at this exciting time of expansion was tempered by concerns over the huge school fees that would be incurred once Archie began his English education at Stowe later the same year. 'I hope the new partnership with Piers will thrive,' he wrote, 'but with new camps in Meru and the Mara and general expansion, I am not sure what the next few years hold, but we shall have to try and keep busy just to keep on top of the school fees. We have an amazing lifestyle, but it does have its downsides.'

* CHAPTER SIXTEEN *

Sosian Transformed

AT the same time that Offbeat Mara and Offbeat Meru were taking off, the work of Christl von Plessen and her builders at Sosian was also nearing completion. By 2004, the original ranch house built by Italian prisoners of war in the early 1940s had been transformed into a spacious and contemporary lodge, where paying guests can relax surrounded by an eclectic mix of African and Argentine artefacts. They start the day with an early morning ride or game drive, returning to breakfast on a wide veranda overlooking the Ewaso Narok River basin, which is separated from wild bushland by an acre of green lawn, where the horses are often turned out to graze.

Elsewhere inside the lodge, a full-sized billiard table stands on the polished parquet floor of a room that was haunted by the ghost of a former owner. Major Gerald Edward's grave is marked by a white stone in the garden, and until his spirit was exorcised, door knobs were sometimes heard rattling in the dead of night, along with mysterious footsteps in the corridor outside.

Visitors no longer sleep in the main house, but in the four stone cottages built by Hannes Nel, which are connected by paved walkways meandering across the lawns. A swimming pool built to the same insect-friendly specifications as the one at Deloraine occupies a sheltered position beyond the cottages, and is overlooked by a towering thatched cabana. Guests are welcomed here with a cold drink after landing on the bush airstrip close by, and return to the pool area for long, shady lunches at the hottest time of day. There are also stables, a tennis court, and four-wheel-drive vehicles to take them out on early morning and late afternoon game drives.

Sosian Lodge started out on the long road to success with Hannes' wife, Lorian, at the helm as manageress, ably assisted by David Macharia, who continues to combine the demanding roles of head waiter, butler, housekeeper, gardener and general Jack-of-all-trades. The kitchen is still run by Niko Mosota from western Kenya, who remembers that fish cakes with avocado and tomato salad was Tristan's favourite dish, and his absolute insistence on all beef being served rare.

After the long-awaited rains arrived at Sosian, the wildlife reappeared as if by magic and Tristan's diaries are packed with references to game spotted on the ranch. 'See elephant on Sosian every day,' he noted in 2002, and a couple of years later was able to count two hundred and fifty from the air, where four years earlier there had been none. Buffalo suffer terribly during a drought and Tristan was particularly proud of their successful return to Sosian, and steady increase in numbers from a drought-stricken low of some forty animals to a thriving herd of more than ten times that number.

Populations of non-migratory species such as giraffe, warthog, impala, waterbuck, wild dog, and the big cats have also increased year on year, although eland, hartebeest and other grazing animals that move with the rains have fared less well, as they are targeted for bush meat when moving onto community-owned land elsewhere in Laikipia. These were spectacular results from a conservation perspective and a tribute to the low-impact ranching policy Sosian's shareholders had agreed from the outset.

Once her high, grassy plains, steep escarpments and river valleys had been properly explored, Sosian's own special attractions became apparent. Visitors can enjoy a ride or drive to the lovely Acacia Dam for a picnic lunch in the company of wildlife arriving for a drink of their own, or a walk into a steep gorge concealing the Samburumburu lugga and a different treasure trove of wildlife on every visit. High waterfalls on the Ewaso Narok River are a magnet for thrill-seekers jumping from a rocky ledge into a deep brown pool thirty foot below, and were a major attraction at Jonti and Juge Barclay's wedding in 2005. Their party was the first of many big events celebrated at Sosian over the years; the lodge was full to capacity and twenty others slept in tented accommodation at Tristan's

Camp beside the river. 'Sosian, Jonti–Juge wedding, waterfall jumping, great fun,' Tristan commented in his diary at the end of a perfect day.

Collectively, the Sosian shareholders embraced a wealth of experience relevant to tourism and conservation initiatives, for there were authorities amongst them on tourism, hospitality and marketing, wildlife and conservation, horses, farming, finance and business. With such a diverse range of knowledge and expertise to draw on, Tristan was frustrated that six years after purchase, Sosian was still not turning in a profit. 'We have just had our shareholders AGM at the ranch, which went OK if you like counting losses and although the ranch looks beautiful, it's a long way from breaking even,' he complained to Rufus in 2006. 'Game and everything else is fantastic, but we are not full of tourists yet and the cattle do not make money at present either.'

Hannes and Lorian Nel had been round pegs in round holes during the development of Sosian, but by the time of Tristan's letter, it was obvious Hannes was more interested in fattening cattle rather than establishing the pedigree herd Tristan preferred, and that he found the burdens of administration and office work increasingly challenging. Lorian had made a good start with the lodge, but she too was ready to move on. Their input into the development of Sosian Ranch and the building of cottages, swimming pool, and shareholders' houses had been nothing short of brilliant according to the shareholders, but they all recognised Sosian had outgrown the rugged frontiersman, who left to build roads in Sudan.

Finding a suitable couple to replace the Nels was a daunting task, but investors struck gold when recruiting twenty-six-year-old Sean Outram and his vivacious girlfriend Charlotte Roger-Smith from Kuki Gallman's ranch nearby. It would have been hard to find anyone better suited to establishing a herd of pedigree cattle than the fourth-generation Kenyan, six-and-a-half-foot giant of a man, who had completed his education at the Royal Agricultural College in Cirencester and spent much of his childhood on safari. Charlotte took on running the lodge, with David Macharia providing continuity behind the scenes, leaving Sean to found the Sosian Boran Stud herd from a nucleus of seventy-six cows selected from Gilfrid Powys's neighbouring Suyian Ranch.

Sosian could comfortably carry many more cattle than the initial wildlife-friendly stocking rate of one cow per twenty acres, but the ratio was increased slightly when it became clear the property was undergrazed. Ultra-low stocking densities resulted in acres of unpalatable grass being shunned by cattle and avoided by timid plains game, since the thick cover allowed predators to creep up on them without warning. An experiment to designate cattle-free zones on the ranch also backfired; the pasture ran to seed and had to be burnt off to stimulate regeneration.

Lower than normal stocking rates resulted in surplus grass at Sosian during the lean grazing months of a dry season, which native pastoralists found impossible to resist after their own overstocked lands had been exhausted. Sean learnt to tolerate trespassers, despite the frustrations of seeing his carefully nurtured pasture eaten off by other men's livestock, but the illegal herders returned home once the rains arrived to lacquer Laikipia green with fresh grass.

Tristan took a close interest in the stud's development, which was kick-started by the purchase of a registered stud bull (inevitably, perhaps, called Tristan), along with other cows and bulls from local breeders. Tristan the bull was supplied by the Voorspuys' old friend, Jackie Kenyon from Mogwooni Ranch, and produced fifty-one calves before being killed by lions in his first season. The great bull's untimely death brought into sharp focus the hazards of combining wildlife with cattle farming, for domestic livestock represents easy prey for the big cats and other predators.

Leopard and lion had been ruthlessly poisoned elsewhere in Laikipia, but Tristan and Sean were determined to find a way of safeguarding their Boran cattle while maintaining a healthy population of big cats. The cattle are under the constant supervision of herders during the day, who have been known to chase off lion with only a wooden knobkerrie[42] for protection. A prize stud cow at Sosian once gave birth to a healthy calf within an hour of being flattened by a lioness, which had been driven from its potential meal by a brave Turkana herder armed only with sticks and stones.

Native pastoralists such as the Maasai and Samburu have traditionally

---

42 A form of club used mainly in Southern and Eastern Africa. Typically, they have a large knob at one end and can be used for throwing at animals in hunting, or for clubbing an enemy's head.

protected their livestock from nocturnal predators by fastening them into thorn bomas at night, but the gates into these round enclosures are often little more than a tree dragged across the opening, and the thorn walls eventually start to rot and break down. Any such weaknesses are exploited by lion, which move upwind under the cover of darkness to feed the captive animals their scent, while letting out an occasional bloodcurdling roar. If this ploy succeeds, the cattle are panicked into stampeding straight into the teeth and claws of other members of the pride, hiding patiently downwind in ambush. Those not brought down flee into the night, where they can be slaughtered at the leisure of lion, leopard and hyena.

Sean was therefore keen to trial portable and predator-proof metal bomas developed on the nearby Ol Pejeta Conservancy. The six-foot-tall enclosures each hold two hundred cattle, and were such a success that Sosian has suffered few losses since deploying them. After a boma has been moved, lush grass sprouts from the well-manured site, which attracts elephants and other herbivores and transforms the area into a game-viewing hotspot for years afterwards. Before the advent of portable steel pens, boma sites were dictated by the close proximity of thorn trees, but cattle can now be bomaed wherever overgrazed pasture might benefit from a dose of natural fertiliser.

Lion have continued to thrive at Sosian, and now concentrate on hunting natural game instead of domestic livestock, although daily depredations by lion and leopard led to sheep and goats being removed from Sosian in 2008. 'When we first arrived, lion sightings were quite rare,' Sean remembers, 'but with better herding practices and night bomas, we have seen the population at Sosian increase to around forty individuals; they are incredibly relaxed around vehicles, which is just what we want. We have been determined to run livestock and wildlife successfully alongside each other, and avoiding lion conflict is crucial to proving the big cats can coexist with ranching.'

Although Sean was a cattleman first and foremost, he did supervise the expansion of Richard Constant's house from the simple stone construction built by Hannes into a much larger home. Hannes had cleverly combined yellow-barked acacia trees growing onsite into the design, and built a swimming pool shored up on one side by natural rock. Sean added further bedrooms, bathrooms, and a cottage, along with a detached oval office to accommodate the three thousand books Richard shipped out from England after deciding to make his home permanently at Sosian.

Built from local ochre-coloured rocks, the buildings nestled unobtrusively beneath a long ridgeline, close to a tumbledown stone wall marking the boundary between Sosian and Suyian Ranch. Every morning the sun climbed out from behind Mount Kenya to fill the house with light and brighten the distant Aberdare Range of mountains to the south. Surrounded by nature, the home seemed as integral to the wild landscape as green-brown plains running away from jumbled rocks and thorns below the veranda. The rocks were frequented by a large male leopard, which left tell-tale footprints in the garden and was often heard rasping at night. Succulent aloe plants flourished behind the house and were a favourite delicacy for elephants and nectar-loving sunbirds.

Despite their impeccable credentials, Sean and Charlotte had been recruited on a temporary six-month contract only, as Steve and Annabelle Carey had already been engaged to run the lodge. However, their arrival coincided with Offbeat Safari's Nanyuki headquarters closing down and the Outrams agreeing to stay on at Sosian; Charlotte opened a new office to handle safari bookings and Sean continued to develop the ranch.

The Careys spent five years looking after guests at the lodge, and when they left to establish a tourist camp of their own, Sean was promoted to the new and senior position of general manager. Tristan once more demonstrated his knack for matching people with jobs by appointing twenty-six-year-old Simon Kenyon and Richard Constant's daughter, Rosy, to succeed the Careys at the lodge.

Tristan had become close friends with Richard Constant since he joined the Sosian team as an investor, and knew Rosy from her months helping out at Sosian as a school leaver. His association with the Kenyon family reached all the way back to the *Out of Africa* film set in 1985, when he had worked and partied with Jackie Kenyon before either of them was married. Jackie and Mandy's son, Simon, was brought up at Mogwooni and had joined Tristan for his first riding safari in the Mara when still a teenager.

The ride was guided by Mark Laurence, but the tempo increased after the Voorspuy family flew in to join them for New Year's Eve and Tristan took control of the Land Rover, following several festive glasses of champagne, and got hopelessly lost in the dark. Camp was eventually reached when fifteen-year-old Simon established his own guiding credentials by directing the way back. Later that night, a thief was caught after Cindy disturbed him rifling through her possessions. The miscreant was trussed up overnight and questioned the following morning before release, although an American child from the group asked Tristan in all seriousness if he was going to be executed. 'That safari was incredibly old-fashioned and wonderful,' Simon recalls, 'and like something out of a Wilbur Smith novel – I couldn't really believe my eyes.'

A few years later, Simon gashed his face badly in an accident when working for Offbeat Safaris as a back-up rider. Tristan gave the injury a cursory glance and told him to man-up and continue, but took a closer look when they returned to camp and decided the wound 'needed a stitch'. Simon was offered a cocktail of whisky and Panadol to mask the pain, but settled for a dose of horse anaesthetic from the first-aid box.

With the help of a head torch, and reading glasses balanced precariously on the end of his nose, Tristan began stitching up the wound using a needle and thread resembling old fishing line. 'The only problem was the anaesthetic wore off after every stitch, so Tristan had to keep re-injecting me,' Simon remembers, 'but he made a good job of it.'

Simon continued to work for Offbeat Safaris on an ad hoc basis, which allowed him to spend a southern-hemisphere summer in early 2012 helping Jakob von Plessen with his riding safari business in Patagonia. Tristan called Simon within an hour of his return from Argentina to inform him that he had been promoted to join Rosy Constant as full-time joint manager of Sosian Lodge. 'You start work on Monday,' he was told.

'Tristan was a massive believer in giving youth a chance,' Simon remembers, 'and even if I hadn't wanted the job, I don't think I would have been allowed to turn it down.' Simon took up position three days later, and twenty-four hours after that, fifteen paying guests walked into the lodge. Simon and Rosy quickly fell into their respective roles of safari guide and lodge manageress, and by the end of their first season were together as a couple.

Sean's appointment as general manager and the arrival of Simon and Rosy marked the start of four prosperous and successful years at Sosian, during which the herd of pedigree Boran cattle grew to be the largest in Kenya, and the lodge became a busy and popular tourist destination. The accounts were given a boost when the British Army, which was already training nearby, expanded its activities onto the ranch in return for handsome reward, which helped the shareholders to continue prioritising wildlife ahead of commercial farming. A military presence on the ranch also improved security and infrastructure, while the army's activities did not disrupt farming practices or appear to disturb the wildlife in any way.

'Integrating wildlife and commercial livestock farming has not been easy, but it's been well worth it,' says Sean Outram. 'To drive around and see giraffes, zebra and even buffalo wandering amongst our herds of pedigree cattle is an awesome sight, although when buffalo are present, the herder will invariably be found up a tree.' The reward for Jonti Barclay has been proving that tourism and farming can work in unison, which he considers to be a more sustainable way forward than relying on donor funding to preserve habitat, as is the case on some other Laikipian properties.

In 2012, Tristan recorded that Laikipia was home to 6,000 elephant, 250 lion and more than 200 wild dogs, together with healthy populations of the endemic species, and that all these animals were flourishing at Sosian. He pointed out that elephant were once excluded from much of Laikipia by cattle fencing, which has since been removed to provide half a million acres of contiguous land, shared between Sosian and other ranches such as Mugie, Loisaba, Mpala, Ol Donyo Lembere, Ol Maisor, Suyian and Segera. 'As a consequence,' he wrote, 'the region is now home to the second-largest elephant population in Kenya.'

'It is great to think that our mutual connections with the Bowers and Mutara finally brought me to be your neighbour at Sosian,' Tristan wrote to Martin Evans eleven years after buying Sosian. 'We have had such fun there, and although I sometimes wonder what I got myself into, Sean and Charlotte's wedding next week will be a reminder of how lucky we all are to be involved. There is a great atmosphere of well-being at Sosian and it's getting rave reviews.'

Tristan found as much fulfilment in nurturing his vision of farming, wildlife and tourism at Sosian, as from guiding high-octane riding safaris through the Mara. He intended spending his retirement there, and in 2012 there was little sign of clouds gathering amongst his records of wildlife expansion across the ranch and hard-won commercial success, or even a hint that the passion engendered by Sosian and all she stood for would ultimately lead to his downfall.

CHAPTER SEVENTEEN

At the Top of His Game

A DECADE after Tristan had put the consortium together to buy the dilapidated ranch and buildings, Sosian had become an established safari destination, popular with repeat visitors to Kenya, and with small groups of families or friends who took over the entire lodge for the private enjoyment of their party. However, Tristan still believed there was nowhere on earth to match the Masai Mara for sheer quantities of wildlife and majestic *Out of Africa* vistas – a landscape he described as the icing on Kenya's cake. Whatever the success of Sosian, the Mara would always remain the bread and butter of the Voorspuys' livelihood, and was the place every visitor to Kenya wanted to experience first-hand.

Offbeat Mara Camp provides a sublime safari base for non-riders, but Tristan remained resolute in his belief that the best way to enjoy the wilder Mara landscape was from the back of a horse. 'A vehicle belches smoke and noise, must stick to the tracks and is not a pure experience,' he wrote. 'The silence and extra height on horseback is a huge advantage and although the body feels tired after a thirty-mile ride, there is a sense of achievement and exhilaration after a long day in the saddle. The wildlife regards you like another animal and riding close to elephant, or being looked down at by an inquisitive giraffe, is the ultimate game experience. On horses we can access areas that nobody else can reach, and there is always a real spirit of adventure.'

His clients agreed. 'Surpassed even our expectations and I could not see myself doing another vehicle safari after an experience as wonderful as this,' one wrote. 'We had a week of galloping across plains pitted with holes, close encounters with lions, swimming in the Mara with hippos. It was without doubt the most exciting holiday I have ever been on and unforgettable, as is Tristan,' enthused another after her Mara ride. An American client fell in love with Africa through her horse's 'black-tipped ears', and like others in Kenya's thrall, returned as often as she could afford and became close friends with the Voorspuys.

Writers and journalists flew out to Kenya to join Offbeat safaris and report back on their enigmatic owner. 'Tristan Voorspuy is a bit of a legend amongst safari cognoscenti,' declared a correspondent from the *Sunday Times*. 'He takes no prisoners, always pushing a bit closer to wildlife than other guides, relying on instinct and the fact that, in the event of a charge, horses can run faster. And he has eyes like a hawk, recognising every bird and animal by sight and call.' The writer ended by describing her Offbeat riding safari as 'the best sort of holiday, when every sense, physical and mental is fully engaged.'

On a Mara safari, guests fell asleep wondering how the next day could possibly surpass the one that had gone before, and took home memories to last a lifetime. Memories of exhilarating gallops beside giraffe that floated but never ran, elephant eyes blinking from skin furrowed like tree bark, the sound of crunching bones and snarling lion, the tear-stained mask of a staring cheetah, and inevitably, herds of wildebeest smeared thick as black treacle across the plains.

Most would never forget the blue half-light of African dawn and dusk, the camaraderie of danger shared and overcome, or the comforting aroma of wood smoke that lingered on clothes long after the holiday was over. The majestic Masai Mara endured as a backdrop to every memory, unassailably permanent, interminably vast and implausibly rich in wildlife.

But on the cusp of the new millennia, this was a land under threat. Most tourists took the timeless Mara landscape for granted, and had little notion of the work that went on behind the scenes to preserve the vistas and wildlife they had travelled halfway round the world to see. Running a tourist operation in the Mara ecosystem became even harder after the government allowed community-owned land there to be sub-divided into individual plots. Those in possession of title deeds were free to enclose or develop their properties, and to borrow money against their land, which was at risk from speculators if the owner defaulted.

As a consequence, repeat visitors to the Mara may have noticed shiny, corrugated tin huts where there were none before, and incongruous wire fences on grassy plains. Every year cultivated land encroached from the east, until the thorn livestock bomas Tristan had jumped in and out of on top of the escarpment had been replaced by maize and corn. One Offbeat client was so dismayed by the changes she witnessed on a repeat visit to the Mara that she vowed never to return.

Tristan and his colleagues had formed an organisation called Campfire to rent camping spots for tourism from group ranch committees in the early 1990s, but in 2000 the Koyiaki Group Ranch was dissolved and there was no longer a legal agreement in place. The following year, all eight hundred members of the former group ranch were issued with title deeds allowing them to sell, develop or cultivate land, slap in the middle of a globally important ecosystem.

The affected area was home to Tristan's favourite campsite beside the Olare Orok lugga, where the wildlife is free to wander between privately owned property and the protected Masai Mara National Reserve next door. He and the other operators feared buildings, fences and monoculture would ruin the national reserve's important peripheral lands, and believed the only solution was to reach a mutually beneficial agreement with as many landowners as possible.

Offbeat is not permitted to bring horses onto the national reserve, but even if the company had been, Tristan and the proprietors of other safari businesses had no interest in relocating to an area that was already a safe haven for wildlife. It would be infinitely more worthwhile, they agreed, to come to an arrangement with the new landowners to guarantee the survival of a threatened landscape. This led to the formation of the Koiyaki Lemek Wildlife Trust in 2003, which disintegrated into splinter groups of private companies before the formation of Mara North Conservancy (MNC) in 2009, by which time Piers Winkworth's Offbeat Mara Camp close to the Olare Orok lugga was well-established.

He joined Tristan and the owners of nine other low-impact tourist camps in negotiating a fee based on tourist beds available throughout the conservancy, which is distributed amongst Maasai landowners according to the size of their holding. In order to avoid overcrowding, visitors to the 65,000-acre conservancy are limited to a maximum of one tourist per 350 acres of land. In return, the Maasai undertake not to build settlements, kill wildlife, exceed agreed stocking rates, or permit access to non-members. A dedicated team of MNC employees administers the scheme, which includes a cattle-breeding programme and a fund to compensate herders if their livestock is killed by predators.

Former MNC Chairman, Stefano Cheli, describes setting up the conservancy as a long, hard process that will not be complete until the final few landowners have all signed up. Cheli remembers Tristan as a member who supported the conservancy concept from the outset, and someone who could be relied upon to attend meetings, some of them with Maasai leaders beneath a tree on the plains.

'Anybody going into the boutique tourism business does it because they love the way of life and are passionate conservationists,' Stefano says. 'Seeing the Mara carved up and built on hurts us all, and preventing that was very important to Tristan.' Another colleague in the safari business at the time recalls Tristan for his open mindedness and modesty: 'He was a visionary, but never one for beating his own chest; he was much lower key than that and probably achieved more than we ever realised.'

MNC has gone from strength to strength since 2009, and the wildlife-rich landscape surrounding the Offbeat camps at Olare Orok remains almost as beguiling and beautiful as it was when Tristan first rode there in the 1980s. He was particularly proud of the resident lion pride, which are protected by a cattle-free zone and are a near-guaranteed sighting for visitors.

'Our most unique and ongoing achievement,' he wrote in 2012, 'has been the habituation of Mara North Conservancy lion to our horses; both now trust each other and the lion allow us to get extremely close. The Offbeat pride on the Olare Orok stream currently has fourteen cubs, which at eighteen months' old now run up and play. I know they trust and respect us, and of course we respect them, but their behaviour is the culmination of thirty years' habituation through successive generations.' Mara North was one of five conservancies Tristan continued to cross after group ranches had been dissolved, and the routes he pioneered are enjoyed by Offbeat clients to this day.

Although Kenya was at the forefront of global conservation initiatives, until the formation of the Kenya Professional Safari Guides Association (KPSGA) in 1996, anyone could set themselves up as a guide, regardless of their experience or skill. This risked the reputation of Kenya as a safari destination, in contrast to those African countries where guides had been officially rated for years. As a recognised qualification encouraged high standards and reassured clients, Tristan strongly supported the formation of the association and passed his bronze medal exam at the KWS headquarters in Nairobi at the first attempt.

The non-governmental KPSGA is now acknowledged as having raised guiding standards throughout Kenya, to the extent that many tour companies will not employ guides without KPSGA certification. Successful candidates must wait three years before proceeding to the next tier, which allows time to gain further experience in the field, but guides at every level are expected to possess a broad knowledge of wildlife, flora and fauna, as well as a thorough understanding of tourism ethics and conservation.

Tristan was awarded silver soon after the qualification became available in 2000, and sat his gold medal exam over three days in 2012, flying himself into Nairobi's Wilson airport for the assessment after a 'good lunch' at Sosian with Richard Constant. He passed comfortably, gaining the second-highest score of all candidates and joining an elite group of fifteen KPSGA gold-level guides.

Tristan's achievement was the culmination of twenty-nine years continuous professional guiding on foot, in vehicles and on horseback, during which he had shared his knowledge and enthusiasm with more than two thousand clients. He was equally interested in the habits of amphibians, insects and reptiles, as he was with larger big game, and was also fascinated by the flora and fauna of Kenya, attending a botany course at Sosian to improve his understanding of Laikipian trees and plants.

Tristan was also an expert ornithologist, but seldom had time to guide specialist birding safaris. He made an exception in early 2012, organising and guiding an epic two-week birding adventure, which began at Offbeat Meru Camp in Kenya and ended up at Murchison Falls in Uganda. The safari was such an exceptional wildlife experience that Tristan abandoned his usual practice of making brief notes in his diary, and instead wrote up a detailed and animated account of the trip, recording 374 different avian species.

Highlights included a greedy, great spotted cuckoo chick, being waited on by surrogate parents, and shoebill storks at Murchison Falls – 'shoebill at last!' He watched a red-billed hornbill carrying katydids, mantis and grasshoppers back to its nest, but best of all was a close encounter with a Meru elephant carrying hundred-pound tusks. 'He was in full musth,[43] dribbling at the sheath and pretended to be very angry with us, giving two or three mock charges, and those magnificent tusks got within six feet of the Land Rover on two occasions.'

The same written response to an enquiry that confirmed Tristan's love for elephants also provides an unusually detailed insight into his thoughts on guiding, which might surprise the many clients he has inspired over the years. 'I am always very grateful and learn lots from guides who are more knowledgeable than me,' he wrote, 'and am never jealous of these types, but try to learn more and act humbly in their presence.'

He disliked being caught out by intelligent and intuitive clients, but was happy to admit defeat and never fabricated the facts. 'If you are humble and unassuming, you will impress,' he maintained, 'but if you are brash and boorish, you will be caught out.' Tristan believed that the guide was the most important ingredient of any safari, and recognised the challenges of communicating harmoniously with those from different political and national backgrounds.

'A guide needs to be a constant evaluator of human nature and realise that every client and every group are different,' he wrote. 'He or she must be a chameleon capable of adjusting to every situation and safari. Dealing with large groups on riding safaris is always interesting; the common denominator of the horse is a great help, but one is constantly evaluating the situation and each safari varies according to the different characters involved.'

He recognised and accepted the responsibilities of guiding clients through the hazardous African bush on horseback, and did not shirk his

---

43 A periodic condition in bull (male) elephants, characterised by highly aggressive behaviour and accompanied by a large rise in testosterone levels.

moral obligations on the rare occasions when things went seriously wrong. That was the case when an American veteran of several Offbeat rides fell off and broke his neck, when his horse put its foot in a hole during a Mara riding safari. It was clear the man would never walk again and faced a life in paralysis, but Tristan stayed in touch throughout his hospital treatment, and three years later visited him at home during a trip to the USA.

The encounter cannot have been easy for either man, but was followed up with a long and newsy email from Tristan, who was determined to cajole a more positive attitude from his friend. 'I was very encouraged by what I saw of you and whilst physically you are not improving, your mental ability has never faltered and so much of life is cerebral,' he wrote.

Tristan offered to put him in touch with a spinal injuries specialist, and gave examples of friends who had found fulfilment despite the limitations of similar life-changing injuries. 'Let's make the most of life in whatever condition we are in,' he implored. 'Buddy, you have a lot of friends out there and I resolve to introduce you to more. I think about you EVERY day and want you to get positive, as you will probably live another twenty-five years at least.'

Tristan disliked clients that asked pointless or vacuous questions, but he sometimes found it impossible to conceal his contempt for a certain kind of person, or suppress his own, fundamentally different, political views. 'One of my faults is to give withering or sarcastic replies that can be unfair,' he admitted. 'A guide must be wary of people who are idealistically not their type and become aggressive. I read carefully and avoid as much as possible, as there are those who can look for trouble, or at worst a money-back situation to exploit.'

That was possibly the case with a client who returned from Kenya dissatisfied with Tristan after a safari with him in 2010. The man did not address Tristan directly, but according to protocol, wrote to his tour operator to complain about the conduct of his guide, which he claimed tarnished his African experience. 'That we were able to enjoy ourselves,' he wrote, 'was in spite of Tristan Voorspuy and not because of him.' The client's grievances alleged a contempt and disregard for both customers on safari and the coloured Kenyans they encountered during the holiday, which was in stark contrast to Tristan's own stated ethics. The tour operator was informed that Tristan's intolerance led to frequent outbreaks of bad temper or shouting, and that the Offbeat Land Rovers were death traps with bald tyres and bulging side walls.

The complainant may have had the misfortune to encounter Tristan in one too many of his maudlin moods, but other guests did not agree with him. A regular client expressed surprise and amazement that a complaint had been made against Tristan at all. 'I felt that we were a happy group that mixed well together and as ever Tristan was the genial host,' he wrote, in response to a request for feedback. 'To suggest Tristan is a racist is just unbelievable to me, as I have never ever by word or action experienced anything out of order.'

Another rider admitted he had also been on the receiving end of Tristan's caustic wit, but quickly moved on. 'Tristan is not everyone's cup of tea, but then maybe neither am I,' he wrote. 'I saw Tristan with his staff at Deloraine and wardens in game reserves and on those occasions he interacted perfectly normally. Tristan was a brilliant guide and so tongue-in-cheek. There are many sides to him; he sometimes has a rather brusque manner, and in a way he treats you rather like his children, but that's because he is trying to show everyone a good time.'

A married couple issued a joint statement confirming the safari surpassed their wildest expectations, but admitted not knowing quite what to expect from a man whose reputation goes so colourfully before him. 'Tristan is certainly not reckless, and he shows you a lot of fun,' they wrote. 'He has run safaris all his life and is the sort of character you may have to stand up to. The ride was exciting and entertaining, but without shortcuts on safety. Nature is cruel, but was always respected by Tristan, who demonstrated an extraordinary love for Kenya, but understands the difficulties the country faces. I would do another ride with him tomorrow.'

A single lady traveller claimed she arrived home with elephant and hippo manure still on her boots, after what was unquestionably 'the most wonderful, exciting, adrenalin-pumping and awe-inspiring holiday' she had ever undertaken. 'The gently chiding banter from Tristan became a daily source of amusement, as we volunteered each other for the first knock-down question/response of the day,' she revealed. 'I was impressed by the rapport Tristan had with those who worked for him, which seemed to be based on mutual respect and courtesy that has obviously been built up over many years.'

Tristan took exception to the accusations of discrimination, pointing out that he was a cynical misanthrope, which should never be confused with prejudice or racism. He was also deeply upset that someone with whom he had parted on good terms at the airport had not aired his grievances face to face. Nevertheless, he wrote to apologise for any unintended offence. 'Yes, I am very likely a little jaded and can be sarcastic,' he admitted, 'and my style can of course be abrupt. If you find me ignorant, that is interesting and I do not intend to defend myself on that score.' He ended the letter by apologising for failing to detect sensitivities, but reminded the complainant that he appeared to have been enjoying the safari just as much as the other members of the group.

Although he never worked as a guide outside Kenya, Tristan was fond of quoting Mark Twain's observation that travel is fatal to bigotry and prejudice. 'You must always learn from your own travel experiences and be interested in other people's lives,' he wrote. 'A broad knowledge of worldwide current affairs is a huge bonus to a guide, and as you get older, you become more cosmopolitan if you keep travelling.' Having done his first promotional trip to the USA with Cindy in 1990, Tristan never stopped travelling around the world to market his safaris, although he had to wait another twenty years before making it to Mel and Bayard Fox's remote Bitterroot Ranch in Wyoming.

The Foxes' Equitours travel company had remained steadfast supporters of Offbeat ever since Tristan's split with Tony Church, and their son had married a girl he met whilst working for Tristan at Deloraine. The snow had not yet melted by the time of his spring visit and it was bitterly cold, but Tristan was immensely impressed that the indomitable Mel Fox, who had been his companion on the long, dark ride back to camp on his first-ever safari job, had chased off a marauding grizzly bear only minutes before his arrival. Later, he was ecstatic to have seen his first wild wolves and moose in Yellowstone National Park, and was delighted to meet some of the Equitours staff that he and Cindy had been corresponding with for the last twenty-five years.

Tristan once admitted that 'selling is the part I hate most' in reference to running a safari company, but he enjoyed exploring foreign lands on horseback, maintaining that it was important to see how operators from other countries and cultures organised riding holidays. Tristan and Cindy joined the UK travel company, Wild & Exotic, on several research itineraries around the world, including a ten-day ride from Argentina to Chile through the remote Andes Mountains of Patagonia, where Tristan caught trout in clear mountain streams and was uplifted by the sight of soaring condors. The Voorspuys also rode Abyssinian ponies from Addis Ababa to the Blue Nile Gorge in Ethiopia, and found elephant, eland and long-crested eagles on Malawi's high Nyika Plateau.

They enjoyed riding through the cloud forest, white water rafting, and surfing as guests of friends in Costa Rica, and when Tristan visited Australia in 2006, dinner with the high commissioner and a visit to the races were accorded equal status in his diary as the sightings of kangaroos, emu and sulphur-crested cockatoo. The Voorspuys joined Freddie Menzies and other friends to discover what life was like behind the former Iron Curtain on a ride through Hungary in 2011. 'I am glad I was born on the correct side,' Tristan wrote in a letter to his mother-in-law, before revealing, as always, the wildlife seen during the holiday. Their Hungarian escort was criticised for his nose-to-tail style of guiding, and Tristan returned home determined to continue a relaxed approach to the way his own clients rode through the Kenyan bush.

Tristan's many trips abroad also taught him not to compartmentalise anyone according to their nationality, for he believed that every country and society included 'the fascinating and good' as well as 'the dull and bad'.

'I have ridden and visited many countries and all the continents, but still feel I am only scratching the surface and have much more to see, and places I long to visit,' Tristan wrote towards the end of his life, 'but the only place that might come close to Africa is South America. The more remote and un-infested by human beings, the happier I am.'

⚜ CHAPTER EIGHTEEN ⚜

Trouble in Paradise

GUESTS were slow to stir as the early morning sunlight filtered through the fever trees surrounding Tristan's favourite campsite above the Olare Orok lugga on a December Sunday in 2011; perhaps they felt a little weary after following Tristan and his assistant, Kitty Graham, on a long, thirty-mile trek across the Mara from Olare Lamun the previous day.

They had reached their tents by early evening, hot, dusty and tired, but were not allowed to shower until Tristan had shown them a leopard up a nearby tree. After checking out the magnificent big cat, he drove everyone home in the dark, passing a solitary lioness on the way into camp. There were no takers for a game drive after dinner that evening, and only five volunteers to join him and Kitty on a ride at daybreak the following morning.

Game was settling down for the day by the time Tristan turned his horse's head for home towards the end of a relaxed early morning ride, picking his way carefully through rocky ground on the descent to the Olare Orok lugga, but he pulled up halfway down the slope to point out an incongruous grey back disappearing into a thicket beside the stream.

Tristan picked up a narrow track through the dense scrub at the bottom of the hill, instructing guests to follow him in single file past prickly tendrils of wait-a-bit thorn. The small group fell silent as they traipsed one behind another after their guide, but the tranquil scene was suddenly shattered by Tristan screaming at the top of his voice. 'Turn around,' he yelled in a tone of urgency no one had heard before. 'Get out of here. Get out, NOW!'

There was enough space for those at the rear of the string to extricate themselves and gallop off to safety, but Kitty's horse immediately behind Tristan was squeezed between tall walls of thorn, and for a few long seconds was unable to turn around. Kitty realised to her horror that the yawning pink chasm framed by dagger-sized tusks hurtling towards them was the outstretched mouth of a charging hippopotamus; a split second later, the terrifying apparition was eclipsed as Tristan pirouetted round to escape the charge. Tristan bellowed at Kitty to get out of the way, but the hippo's collision with his horse's hindquarters an instant later had an electrifying effect on the petrified gelding, which plunged forward and dropped his rider directly in front of a belligerent hippo weighing every ounce of three thousand pounds.

Tristan instinctively tucked himself into the foetal position and feigned death, as his assailant's broad puffing snout shunted him along the track like a football. He felt strips being torn from the loose folds of his shirt and gritted his teeth in anticipation of being chopped clean in half, but the battering suddenly ceased, and his attacker was gone. Tristan lay still as death for a minute or more before daring to lift his face from the dirt; the hippo had vanished, but Tristan was taking no chances, crawling along on his belly for several yards before rising slowly on shaking legs. His canvas shirt was ripped and damp with saliva, his ribs ached, and the skin of his exposed back stung as if it had been sandpapered.

The others had re-grouped on the open hillside and feared the worst when Tristan's horse came galloping up to join them with the saddle swinging below his belly. Tristan spotted the riders approaching cautiously in the distance, and heard his name shouted across the open space between them. Not wishing to incite a second charge, he waved back and pressed his index finger to his lips in a gesture of silence.

Tristan said little on the short ride to camp, but over breakfast expanded on how it felt to be used as a human football by an animal that claims more lives than any other species in Africa. He was back on his horse the same afternoon, taking his clients much closer than they would have preferred to an elephant carrying hundred-pound tusks.

Tristan wrote to Cindy's mother a few weeks later, revealing that her daughter and son-in-law had both been somewhat in the wars of late. Cindy had fractured her neck at a one-day event, but had remounted to continue and not discovered the extent of her injury until being x-rayed the following day.

He described in detail his own close encounter with the hippopotamus in the Mara. 'With those teeth on the chimneypiece back home at Deloraine,' he wrote, referring to the final seconds of his ordeal, 'the imagination ran wild, but it suddenly went quiet and when I finally braved a peek, the hippo had disappeared. I was very lucky, because they know how to use those teeth.' What Tristan neither wrote nor realised, was that his lucky escape from the hippo's jaws was the last of his nine lives gone. There were none left now; he had used them all up.

Tristan's horses did not always lead the same charmed life as their owner. Although the Voorspuys never lost a horse to hippopotamus or crocodile, several were killed by lion and more still lost to insect-borne diseases. Some, like a grey gelding named Moshi, were only accounted for months after they had gone missing; his horseshoe was spotted attached to the grey stump of a well-chewed fetlock joint by a sharp-eyed guest during a Mara ride.

The worst equine tragedy, however, was the consequence of a lorry crash that occurred in September 2009 *en route* to start a safari. When Jakob von Plessen left Deloraine an hour behind the horse lorry in a Land Rover full of clients, he was looking forward to spending a week in the Mara, and all seemed well with the world. He made good progress across the floor of the Rift Valley, before beginning the long haul up the Mau Escarpment, beyond which lay the Mara's hallowed lands and swarms of migrating game.

The road twists and turns on the steep, thousand-metre climb up the Mau, and as Jakob rounded a tight bend, he was met by a crowd of excitable Africans surrounding the Offbeat lorry, lying on its side fifty metres below the road. Jakob was told the driver and two syces had been taken to hospital by police, but he had already found the crushed body of Topper, Tristan's favourite Border Terrier, lying inside the empty cab and wrenched open the lorry's side door to get at the horses inside.

To his relief, the horses at the front were alive and seemingly unharmed, but the whites of others' eyes glazed lifelessly skywards, and Jakob could see that three more were so badly injured that they would never make it out alive. He had no rifle with which to end their suffering, only a sharp knife. After his grisly work was done, the Argentine guide wiped the blood from his hands and went to comfort clients sobbing inconsolably by the Land Rovers; this was not what they had come to Africa to experience.

At the time of the accident, Tristan was away from home guiding his own group of American clients, but despite his obvious distress on receiving the news, and the Americans' entreaties for him to return to Deloraine, Tristan insisted on completing the safari, and according to one of the guests, 'managed to make it the most fun and memorable trip of our lives.' Meanwhile a lorry was sent the next day from Deloraine with a fresh set of horses, and Jakob's group ended up missing only one ride.

By 2013, things had not been going well for Tristan for some time. In November he had been frogmarched off for interrogation at Gatwick Airport after airport security had discovered rifle bullets in his washbag, which he had uncharacteristically forgotten to remove from their usual place of safe-keeping on safari. He was released after a lengthy interrogation, but the incident was one of several mishaps to have blighted a period that represented a low point in Tristan's life.

The loss of a favourite horse in September was compounded when a ride led by Mark Laurence caused him many complications after a client departed halfway through the safari, and followed up on her return to the UK with a written complaint to her tour operator. Mark, who had returned to guide for Offbeat on an ad hoc basis after his own riding safari venture folded in 2009, had become embroiled in the petty politics of an unusually incompatible group, some of whom also criticised his handling of the situation. As to be expected, Tristan defended his former right-hand man robustly, and pointed out the participants had been unusually fortunate to see all of the Big Five on their safari. He addressed every accusation put before him in detail, but made it clear he was not prepared to offer any refund as demanded by four members of the party.

Tristan was also obliged to explain his own behaviour towards the remainder of the group, when they returned to Deloraine for the usual two-day interlude after the riding safari had ended. According to the tour operator, two clients had found a hostile atmosphere awaiting them at the Voorspuys' family home, and a host who was 'cantankerous and not remotely interested in the issues there had been on the trip.' Cindy came in for criticism, too, after she accosted a complainant having downed one too many vodkas.

At this time, Offbeat Safaris and the couple at its helm should have been entering a new era of prosperity and happiness; the considerable costs of educating Archie and Imo were at last behind them. Imo was about to start reading French and Spanish at Edinburgh University, and Archie was by now a well-travelled and accomplished horseman, with the knowledge and maturity to guide his own clients on Offbeat riding safaris. However, the Voorspuys' marriage had also reached a critically low point after years of steady decline, and both Cindy and Tristan were finding it increasingly difficult to maintain the impressive appearance of the glittering safari couple.

Tristan had written to his mother-in-law, Angela, as far back as 2004, to explain his absence from a family visit to England and reassure her that all was well in the marriage. 'I am completely devoted to your lovely daughter,' he wrote, 'and although we are not always in agreement I know she loves me, too, while we are devoted to the children and their upbringing is paramount, so please do not give our marriage a second thought.' A year later he wrote her another long letter and ended by paying tribute to her daughter, while recognising the disadvantages of unavoidable but lengthy absences from home and family.

'And of course, thank you for Cindy, who is such a fantastically brought-up and beautiful wife,' he enthused. 'We could never have got where we are without her calm efficiency and she has brought up two beautiful children as a very hands-on mother. As much hands on as I am hands off with safari life, and not such attention to detail as far as they are concerned.'

The deterioration in the Voorspuys' marriage six year later is clearly documented in Tristan's diaries; where he used to record wedding anniversaries and write 'home x 4 bliss', from 2011 onwards his time at Deloraine is frequently recorded as 'home alone', 'awful fights' and 'things could be better', and finally by 2013, 'home x 1 bliss'. The reality was that both Cindy and Tristan were reaching the end of their tether, after nearly twenty-four punishing years of continuous safaris, entertaining and travel, during which there had been little or no spare time for one another.

Tristan's relentless drive and conservation initiatives kept him fully occupied and away from Deloraine for weeks on end, and despite an innate resilience, the effects of a hard, physical life were beginning to catch up with him. 'Tristan often returned exhausted after back-to-back safaris,' Cindy recalls, 'and then had little time to catch up on all his many projects before it was time to leave again for the next one.'

The pressures of a lifestyle where both partners in the marriage are frequently separated for long periods of time are obvious, but the job that kept Tristan from Deloraine was uniquely varied, exciting and dangerous. Extensive knowledge of wildlife and nature commensurate with thirty years of guiding African safaris garnered Tristan respect and admiration from clients, and his strong, decisive, and often fearless leadership commanded their trust and attention.

Tristan's circumspect manner and lack of tolerance was not to everyone's liking, but for most of his clients, he was a man of alluring contradictions. Many enjoyed his sharp wit, intellect and wisdom, but also his love of adventure and a sense of humour that occasionally dissolved into uncontrollable and contagious laughter. When combined with Tristan's rugged good looks, African sunshine, and the thrills and camaraderie of a horseback safari amongst wild game, these traits were the ingredients of an intoxicating cocktail that sometimes led to inevitable consequences.

'As we progressed on our route, my admiration and confidence in Tristan grew daily,' one female admirer wrote, after returning from safari. 'Having shrewdly assessed our combined capabilities, he took us just close enough to smell and taste danger, which was, I think, what we all secretly hungered for, yet I felt he was always in control of our safety.' Another described him as 'devastatingly handsome, tanned and fit, with a love of life and boyish sense of adventure.'

Others were more to the point and corresponded with their guide directly after returning from holiday. 'Of course I have a crush, and the guide is king and gets the chick, but that's just a different manifestation of fat London bankers pulling the girls like they do, the only difference is that London goes on, whereas for most of us, safari does not,' lamented one. 'You have a pulling power most men can only dream of.'

Tristan was not immune to the attention of attractive female admirers, and over the years had succumbed to the occasional safari indiscretion, or as a Kenyan friend put it, 'Tristan had a bit too much testosterone running through his veins, which didn't do him any good.' Any indiscretions remained exactly that; friendships ignited on safari were invariably let down gently and with courtesy after the holiday had ended, for Tristan never contemplated a life without Cindy. 'I am accomplished at dishing out the gentle rejections, but I just don't know how to behave myself when the boot is on the other foot,' wrote an outmanoeuvred admirer, after Tristan had tactfully declined to see her during one of his many trips back to the UK.

When a disgruntled partner called Cindy to condemn Tristan's behaviour, Cindy found herself apologising on her husband's behalf in a typically sang-froid fashion, for she believed Tristan to be occasionally unfaithful but fundamentally loyal. She was more perturbed by his tendency to take her for granted, and having to bear the brunt of his increasingly misanthropic outlook on life, which often surfaced at home at Deloraine. 'I felt as though I was walking on eggshells all the time,' Cindy remembers, 'and I was at a loss as to how to make him happy.'

Despite their problems and the difficulties of communicating on a one-to-one basis with his wife, Tristan remained steadfastly committed to the concept of their marriage. 'I never once heard Tristan speak ill of Cindy,' observed a close mutual friend. 'She meant the world to him, but he forgot to tell her. He was always looking beyond the house and not paying attention to his own backyard. Cindy worked incredibly hard, but was rarely given any credit for her role.' A breakdown in communications led to both Cindy and Tristan taking refuge in alcohol, but Cindy also found solace from the difficulties of her marriage in a relationship with another man.

Despite Cindy's increasing absences from Deloraine, life there continued as normally as possible, for there was still a constant stream of clients and friends to entertain. Twenty-four guests had sat down to celebrate Cindy's fiftieth birthday at Deloraine in August, but within a month, her increased dependency on alcohol and a predilection for hard partying resulted in referral by friends and family to a rehabilitation centre in South Africa.

Tristan had hoped that his wife's twenty-eight-day stay at the Cape Town clinic would not only cure her of any dependencies, but also result in the breakup of her affair. He was relieved that Cindy's stay in South Africa marked a turning point on her road to recovery, but was bitterly disappointed by his wife's decision to build a life with another man. Tristan continued to welcome her spasmodic visits to Deloraine, and her interaction with the horses there.

'When Cindy was back from rehab, all Tristan could do was talk to me of her wonderful riding skills at the Naivasha Sanctuary Farm Event,' remembers Lucy Camm. 'Not a word of criticism, he stood by her loyally even when she was with another man, wanting me to watch her with him and notice her wonderful riding skills.'

Tristan may have remained proud of his wife, but he was often miserable and troubled by a situation over which he had no control. When sharing these concerns with close friends and family, he communicated candidly and honestly.

'You wonder about my marriage which seems to have gone beyond recall, which I hoped would not be the case,' he wrote to one in an email in November 2014. 'I must be a bit of a taskmaster and Cindy claims she was worn down by it all. We both had a couple of infidelities over the years and I was probably more to blame, though never dreamed I would lose her until an older x 4 married man quietly moved in over a long period and without my noticing, by which time it was too late. We have always had enforced absences over the years, although also did many safaris together.'

Apart from the very occasional reference such as 'home x 3 in office, going mad', Tristan's diaries offer little clue as to his inner turmoil during this time of his life. But those close to Tristan recognised the signs. 'Cindy's the love of my life, you know,' he told Hector Camm on a long journey back from Arusha in early 2014. 'You could see it all meant a great deal to him,' Hector remembers.

Others recalled Tristan as being 'in a pretty dark place' and 'not knowing whether he was coming or going.' Against this backdrop, Tristan offered to sell Offbeat Safaris to Jakob von Plessen and Simon Kenyon, but the sale never went ahead after Tristan's protégés had a long, hard think about the ethics and consequences of buying the business and decided not to proceed.

Despite the troubles, riding safaris continued apace; some were led by Archie, Jakob or a freelancing Mark Laurence, but Tristan continued to guide back-to-back riding safaris, and remained enraptured by wildlife encounters throughout the dark days of Cindy's absence from Deloraine. Stunning orchid spiders, leopards on a kill up a tree, elephant and lion are all recorded in his diaries, as are a visit to Uganda to watch mountain gorillas, tiger fishing in the lower Zambezi Valley, and a marketing trip to West Palm Beach. As if Tristan did not have enough on his plate, in December 2014 he flew down to Kibwezi on the edge of Tsavo East National Park with Freddie Menzies, to inspect a two-hundred-acre tree farm the two friends had recently bought together.

Meanwhile, trouble was brewing up in Laikipia, where the first stirrings of an ultimately catastrophic movement for the Voorspuy family were beginning to gather pace. Initially, there was little cause for concern over events taking place on the eastern and western fringes of Laikipia following the 2013 elections.

Since the early 2000s, Pokot livestock herders from the Baringo region had been intermittently invading Kikuyu smallholdings straddling the border with Baringo and the Laikipia Nature Conservancy's southern boundary, although there had been a marked increase in aggression and frequency during the 2007 election year.

Armed invasions of private property on the eastern and western fringes of Laikipia started to escalate again during the 2013 general election, at which Mathew Lempurkel was voted in as the Orange Democratic Movement party's MP for Laikipia North. Kenya's devolved constitution, which established county governments to distribute each of Kenya's many tribes a fair share of government revenues, also came into effect that year. The ruling incentivised local groups to infiltrate, influence and control county governments and their revenues ahead of any elections.

The 2013 election year also marked the beginning of an alliance between the Pokot and their traditional enemies from the north, the Samburu, who joined forces to invade, steal livestock, and attack residents inhabiting the large swathe of land surrounding villages to the west of

Rumuruti. This area of Laikipia is sometimes referred to as the abandoned land, since many of the title-deed holders have left the area, and is chiefly made up of small, subsistence farmers from the southern Kikuyu tribe.

Some group ranches in eastern Laikipia also experienced an increase in illegal grazing incidents after Lempurkel's victory, but the first major invasion of a private ranch did not take place until 2015, when Samburu morans and their livestock moved onto the sixty-thousand-acre Loisaba Conservancy.

Illegal occupation of community land in 2013 did not trouble Tristan unduly – apart from anything else, he had enough problems of his own that year – but the 2015 invasion of the large, privately owned Loisaba was a very different matter. The conservancy was only separated from Sosian by Gilfrid Powys's 44,000-acre Suyian Ranch to the east, where Archie had been appointed farm manager in charge of 150 employees and 3,500 cattle.

Sosian had experienced her share of illegal grazing in the past, but the arrival of cattle and their herders from neighbouring community-owned lands to the north and south had always coincided with a shortage of pasture during the dry season. Sosian's general manager, Sean Outram, adopted a pragmatic approach to these inconveniences, which would have been impossible to confront without expensive and comprehensive security.

But the much larger and significantly more aggressive invasion of Loisaba Conservancy by herders wielding AK-47 assault rifles was yet another blow to Tristan, who was by then living alone at Deloraine surrounded by problems on all sides.

CHAPTER NINETEEN

Game Over

IRONICALLY, the 2015 invasion of Loisaba also marked the turning point in Tristan and Cindy's marriage after nearly two-and-a-half difficult years. Cindy organised and attended a party to celebrate Tristan's sixtieth and Imo's twenty-first birthdays in July, at which two hundred and forty family and friends sat down to a three-course dinner in a marquee pitched on the front lawn. Guests wore black tie at the 1920s themed party, were welcomed with champagne cocktails, dined on Deloraine lamb and danced until sunrise.

Tristan was seated between his old friends Elizabeth Ryrie and Mandy Kenyon and later described the evening as 'a fabulous do, Deloraine is a special place to throw bashes like that.' Four months later, Cindy and her on-off companion of the last two years evaluated their situation and parted amicably.

Cindy's return to Deloraine at the very start of 2016 was welcomed by Tristan, who anticipated a new era of stability and optimism, tempered perhaps, with a little caution. He wrote to Cindy's parents in January 2016 to thank them for their usual Christmas present of a Smythson Badminton diary, and to reflect on the recent difficulties in his marriage. He explained that safari bookings had been slow for the last couple of years and revealed the 'constant worry' of maintaining Deloraine and a large string of horses, which he acknowledged was compounded by his naturally cynical nature.

'So I probably take it out on my nearest and dearest,' he admitted. 'Cindy and I get on a lot better than we used to, as we have years of living together to reflect on, but I lost the vision of marriage I'm afraid and it is far more a business affair. That having been said, we are working well together and I still count you very much as my in-laws and as family and of course I want Cindy to be happy and fulfilled.'

Tristan expressed optimism for the future, but candidly revealed the extent to which his spirits sank during his lengthy separation from their daughter. 'I have struggled on and kept up appearances for the business's sake,' he wrote, 'but I do not mind telling you it has been hard, and I think we both came as close to breakdown as possible at different times. That Cindy is no longer drinking is wonderful, but I'm afraid I still drink for fun. There is no point in making rash decisions about anything yet, just let time heal the wounds.'

He was upbeat about the prospects for Sosian, and concluded his letter by reflecting that the enterprise 'is doing so well with Sean and Charlotte and Simon and Rosy. The cattle and the lodge with its game tourism are really coming into their own and I can now concentrate on building a house at Sosian, where I can go and retire when the time comes.'

Tristan also emailed an American friend called Anne Buckley, who spent several months working for Offbeat as a back-up rider. 'It's been a bit of a struggle with lean years caused by a combination of Kenya's reputation and my personal life with Cindy, for which I am much to blame,' he wrote, 'but her addiction and stepping out of my life was tough going. 50 staff and 60 horses on your own is a tall order and so a business suffers, especially when you are mentally challenged by it too.'

In May, Tristan visited America for another marketing trip and stayed with Anne and her family in Nashville for a hunt ball, where he danced all night in the velvet dinner jacket he had brought out from Deloraine. 'We talked about how happy he was to have Cindy home again,' Anne remembers, 'he seemed to be in such a good place.' Tristan flew back to the UK to represent Offbeat on the African Horse Safari Association stand at Badminton Horse Trials, where he welcomed visitors in warm May sunshine and learnt of renewed confidence in Kenya. He returned to Deloraine primed and ready for the forthcoming riding safari season, which was to include Offbeat's first-ever group of Chinese clients.

Tristan revived what he termed 'that great old concept' of sending Christmas cards at the end of 2016, noting that it must be good for business, and that the email version is 'far too cheapskate and almost an insult, there is nothing better than a card or letter arriving through the post.' Although he touched on the problems facing Laikipia in many of the cards he sent, there was no disguising his renewed optimism and energy. Cindy was back home for good, Offbeat had enjoyed the best safari season for some years, and at a remarkably young age, Archie had landed one of the top cattle-ranching jobs in Kenya. Imo had graduated from Edinburgh, and the Deloraine stables were bursting with the sort of equine talent that other yards could only dream of.

The Voorspuys spent a family Christmas together at Deloraine and saw in the New Year on a Mara riding safari. 'Red letter day. Find rhino on way down. Cross river, 12 lion,' reads Tristan's diary entry for the first day of a new year. Imo had to leave before the holiday ended, but was denied a vehicle and told to ride to the bush airstrip on horseback instead. She trotted off happily to catch the plane, accompanied by a syce to bring her conveyance back to camp. 2017 could hardly have got off to a better start.

Tristan packed so much into the first two months of the year that anyone reading his diary could be forgiven for assuming he was living each day as if it were his last. The family safari in January was followed by an Amboseli ride close to the Tanzanian border at the end of the month. The group was assembled by the Voorspuys' old friend and loyal supporter of Offbeat Safaris, Lucinda Green, and included another red-letter day when Offbeat's Maasai spotter, Nettie, found four lion at Soit Nado.

At the beginning of February, Tristan flew down to Botswana to accompany a small group of clients on a birding safari at Kujwana, in the Okavango Delta, and was rewarded by finding a rare Pel's fishing owl. Tristan made a point of visiting an elderly Sonia Ryrie at Rosslyn when he returned from Botswana. New houses and gardens had replaced the views of open countryside and coffee plantations that greeted him in 1977, but flowers in the stone-flagged courtyard were still shaded by the mulberry tree, and inside, the house had lost none of its timeless colonial charm.

Rosslyn held a special place in Tristan's affections and he wrote to Sonia's daughter, Elizabeth, soon afterwards offering advice and suggestions for its future. 'Tristan could be complicated and was so detached later in life, but he was still deep down the Tristan I had always known,' Elizabeth remembers, 'a true loyal friend to me from when I first met him aged seventeen.'

In contrast to Tristan's personal life, the Laikipia situation was rapidly deteriorating. A school and Catholic community centre in Mutamaiyu, adjacent to Martin Evans's Ol Maisor Ranch, had been attacked and destroyed by invaders in May 2016, and two months later Segera Ranch, immediately to the south of Sosian, was invaded by armed Samburu tribespeople from neighbouring communities, reinforced by hordes of aggressive Pokot.

The shooting and wounding of a Samburu moran, after he had thrown a spear at a Segera security officer, led to a ten-day confrontation between police and invaders, but the ranch's water and pasture were exhausted by the end of 2016, and the invaders retreated. Lombala Ranch, owned by relatives of former Kenyan president Mwai Kibaki, was also invaded in July by Samburu, who shot and injured the manager before overrunning and occupying the ranch.

These invasions, which were the precursor of something much more serious, had begun many months before the first signs of a drought emerged after the failure of the short November rains. It was an election year in 2017, and from early January onwards, invasions of private property escalated sharply in scale of numbers and violence. On 9th January, Pokot and Samburu invaders overwhelmed the 49,000-acre Mugie Conservancy, a rhino sanctuary protected by KWS forces immediately to the north of Sosian. They stole four hundred head of cattle and murdered two members of staff, in retaliation for the non-fatal shooting of an armed Pokot during a running battle with the KWS.

The Pokot, natural hunters from the Baringo region of Kenya, used to killing big game with a bow and arrow as an initiation into manhood, directed their bullets at the conservancy's wildlife, slaughtering elephant, buffalo and giraffe with impunity. Three weeks later, many of them left Mugie's depleted pastures and followed members of the Laikipiak Maasai community south onto Gilfrid Powys's Suyian, where Archie was now managing the ranch.

Police forces were called in to defend the property, but they were heavily outnumbered, and a tourist lodge owned by Gilfrid's daughter and third-generation Kenyan, Anne, was looted and burnt down after one of the invading morans was shot dead at the end of January. Tristan flew up to Sosian to assess the situation, and on his return to Deloraine he emailed Sam Kiley, a foreign correspondent at Sky News, imploring him to visit Laikipia and offering his services as a guide.

'We are on the front line in the current invasions,' he wrote. 'Sadly there is no government interest, but so much at stake and so little press on an urgent situation. It is a Mugabe-style invasion, and as a shareholder in the thick of all this with so much to lose, I feel I am more than qualified to assist you. I have ridden and flown the length and breadth of Laikipia many times and plan to build my retirement home at Sosian. Please take this seriously as I am very worried for the future of Kenya and am very aware of the ramifications of these land invasions. The bottom line is overpopulation and degradation of traditional tribal grazing lands.'

Perhaps Sky News footage of elephants rotting in pools of their own blood, or buffalo with just a sliver of hide peeled away from their bloated corpses, would have made a difference, but for whatever reason, Sky News did not come in time.

With the situation spiralling dangerously out of control and at Sean Outram's insistence, on 1st February a decision was taken to temporarily close down Sosian Lodge in the interests of guests' safety. Tristan did not agree this was necessarily the best way forward and clashed with his general manager over the issue, even though it was in line with the latest Foreign Office advice to avoid travel to western Laikipia. The day after Sosian shut down, Tony Church wrote to Fred Kaigua, the chief executive of KATO, asking for his intervention at the highest level to prevent ongoing lawlessness in Laikipia, which he described as a national crisis.

His pleas elicited a response several weeks later from Richard Leakey, head of KWS, explaining that his organisation's role in Laikipia was to protect rhino, and not to act as tourist police or regular law enforcement. This policy helped to safeguard rhino sanctuaries in Laikipia such as Borana, Lewa, Ol Pejeta and Ol Jogi, but was of little comfort to Sosian shareholders and staff, whose ranch was rich in every other species of wildlife, but had no rhino.

At this time Tristan also exchanged emails with a UK tour operator, who had taken issue with the word 'invasion' being used to describe armed entry onto private property by herders and their livestock.

'There was no grass or game on the farm when I put a consortium together to purchase Sosian from a bank in 1999,' he reminded his correspondent, 'but we now have 1,800 head of cattle, employ 150 people and pay \$200,000 in tax every year. It is a culmination of 18 years of love and investment, but we are bracing ourselves for an armed walk-on any day now. Yes, the northern tribes are desperate in the latest, but by no means catastrophic, drought and six years of reasonable rain have allowed them to overstock with their domestic stock, while fat cats from the same ethnicity put stolen money into livestock as an untraceable asset. The degradation of the fragile Northern sandy soils which supported man, livestock and game for thousands of years is nearly complete and will take decades to recover if it was ever allowed to. If the Laikipia ranch owners upped and left, these people would be happy for a very short space of time, as they swamped the land and destroyed every last blade of grass. Sadly Laikipia and Kenya is one small example of the greatest challenge mankind has yet faced. What chance for the wildlife and tourism, yet alone ourselves, in the long run?'

Tristan's prediction became reality in mid-February, when a gradual dispersal of invaders and approximately 100,000 head of their cattle from Mugie and Suyian Ranches to Sosian got underway, characterised by the established pattern of aggressive confrontation with ranch and security staff and indiscriminate destruction of wildlife. The livestock herders were attracted to Sosian by an excess of dry-season grass, which was a direct consequence of careful management and low stocking rates designed to encourage wildlife, but they were also incentivised by politicians in an election year, promising land access, cattle and weapons in exchange for political loyalty and electoral votes.

As the ownership of cattle can be traced by their brand, it had become clear during earlier invasions that large herds belonging to a few wealthy individuals were being tended by impoverished morans in exchange for cash, guns, food and alcohol. Cattle are not just a symbol of wealth and status; they can also be used as a vehicle for concealing dubious earnings. For trespassers, they are a lucrative commodity, unburdened by the costs of owning or managing the land on which they graze.

When Sosian was overrun in early 2017, Mathew Lempurkel was the incumbent MP for Laikipia North, whose campaign T-shirts bore the slogan 'Shield of Cattle'. His political career has been overshadowed by controversy, including accusations of stealing charity funds and equipment. Famously misogynistic and aggressive, Lempurkel had physically assaulted his female political rival only three months before the Sosian walk-on, and followed up after his arrest by sending her a threatening and abusive text message. He was to be identified as a man whose name has been raised by 'every single invasion victim regardless of tribe, area or acreage' in a report on political violence, land invasions and forced displacements in Laikipia County that was published in May 2017.

The Pokot MP for Baringo, Asman Kamama, has also been widely accused of inciting his fellow tribesmen to steal cattle and invade private property in Baringo and Laikipia, and of using his position on the government security committee to delay and obstruct government intervention. Trespassing cattle were not the exclusive domain of politicians, many were owned by businessmen such as the wealthy African tribesman residing in Switzerland, who in January 2017 appeared at Mugie Conservancy in a four-wheel-drive vehicle to check up on his herd.

Losing the occasional elephant or other game to poaching had been an ongoing problem throughout Sean's time at Sosian, as witnessed by a large map on his office wall, where the site of each elephant death is marked by a red pin, but the scale of slaughter and gratuitous cruelty following the February invasion was unlike anything Sean had ever seen before. Being government-owned and privately protected, Sosian's wildlife stood for everything the invaders despised. Sean and his staff became accustomed to the sound of gunshot several times a day, every day, in a spree of indiscriminate slaughter where every animal from the tiny dik-dik to the mighty elephant was considered fair game.

Many animals were left to rot where they fell, although Sosian staff found some carcasses with strips of skin peeled from the flanks of dead buffalo, or testicles removed, which hinted at a revival of witchcraft customs Tristan believed had long since disappeared. 'Some Pokot rituals of grisly warrior status involving big game long since extirpated in their own lands, have been revived,' he revealed in a letter, 'elephant, buffalo, giraffe and other game has been shot and mutilated to rekindle lost customs that we thought were gone forever.'

Pokot invaders speared and abandoned a baby buffalo to its fate in the dam below Richard Constant's house, and of the fifteen elephants killed on Sosian during their occupation, three were so young they had not yet sprouted tusks. Towards the end of February, a female elephant was discovered suffering from a broken shoulder, an injury that Sean describes as a death sentence, but despite her horrific wounds, the matriarch had survived for several days, protecting her tiny calf throughout.

Sean found the three-month-old elephant cowering beneath its mother's shrunken belly and caked black from her dried blood. A KWS vet darted and rescued the baby, but in order to reduce an orphan's trauma, the distraught mother was not shot dead until her calf had first lost consciousness. News of this and other wildlife tragedies troubled Tristan terribly, but he was powerless to prevent the destruction of eighteen years' endeavour to provide a safe habitat for all wildlife at Sosian.

* CHAPTER TWENTY *

The Last Ride

ON 1st March, Tristan joined Joanna Westermark in Tanzania on an exploratory ride across the eastern Serengeti Plain, the same day as Sean Outram arrived in Uganda to honour a similarly long-standing commitment at Murchison Falls, while his wife, Charlotte, was on holiday with their children at the coast. Although Sosian was occupied by hostile armed herders and their livestock, Sean could see no reason to cancel his short visit to Uganda, for the police had repeatedly failed to intervene and the situation appeared deadlocked for the foreseeable future.

In Barend Lamprecht, he had chosen an experienced and competent person to hold the fort until his return. Married to Martin Evans's niece and based at Ol Maisor, the tough forty-one-year-old South African with close-cropped hair looks every inch the dependable frontiersman and is also a qualified safari guide.

Sean's break was to be cut short, for on reaching Murchison Falls he received news that a large police deployment would be sent to Sosian early the following morning. This time they turned up as promised, arriving in Land Cruisers, trucks and an armoured car, before heading towards Richard Constant's house with the intention of clearing cattle and trespassers from a two-kilometre ridgeline behind the property.

The house stands alone in wild country nearly three miles from the Sosian Lodge headquarters, and is surrounded by dense, thorny scrub, providing ideal cover to an enemy armed with AK-47 assault rifles and emboldened by their Laibon's assurance that government bullets could do them no harm. Despite the advantage of an armoured car, two hundred and fifty largely inexperienced police were no match for hardened Pokot and Samburu bush fighters occupying a superior position, and they were ordered to retreat back to Sosian Lodge after one of them was grazed in the head by an enemy bullet.

The police withdrawal left Richard's house vulnerable to nocturnal attack, but Sosian's stalwart head of security, Saimon Eturen, arranged for the staff there to be evacuated under the cover of darkness. As the police deemed the operation to be too risky, Saimon and Barend Lamprecht chanced their own lives to reach the rendezvous on time and complete a successful rescue operation. Later that night, a lorry rolled up outside the abandoned house, and was loaded up with Richard's furniture and effects before being driven off towards the community lands to the east.

With Sosian commandeered as a police battle headquarters, the lodge managers Simon and Rosy, together with Rosy's mother and an English helper, had already left and reached the Kenyon's Mogwooni Ranch an hour's drive away in safety. Shortly after 11.00 p.m., staff at Teresa Orme-Smith's house were alerted by the sound of gunfire that later transpired to be the killing of another buffalo, and fled into the night.

The house was looted and burnt to the ground soon afterwards, along with Christl von Plessen's home nearby. Christl was with Gilfrid Powys at the time, but they managed to escape with her staff and were discovered sheltering in their car by Barend at first light the following morning.

The police commander flew into Sosian by helicopter early the next day, but was reluctant to discuss events of the previous night with Barend, or to send his men to protect the only shareholder's house that had not yet been razed to the ground. When Sean arrived back from Uganda shortly after midday, along with Jonti Barclay, he also urged the commander to defend Richard's house, but was reminded the police were there to protect people and not buildings. At 3.00 p.m. that afternoon, a column of thick black smoke spiralled into the clear blue sky above a ridgeline still bristling with armed men eager for battle. Richard's house had gone up in flames.

As soon as news of the arson attack on Teresa and Christl's houses reached Tristan in the Serengeti that Friday morning, he resolved to abandon his riding safari and make his way to Sosian as quickly as possible. His own plane was temporarily grounded, but he found a pilot who was willing to fly him back to Nairobi at short notice. As he was waiting at Kilimanjaro airport, Tristan's telephone rang with the news that Richard's house had also fallen to arson. This was a devastating blow, since Tristan felt personally responsible for bringing him on board, and Richard had also made the life-changing decision to make Sosian his permanent home.

Despite his anxiety, Tristan's enthusiasm for the safari he had left behind was undiminished when he spoke to Piers Winkworth before boarding the plane, raving about cheetahs hunting for fun, thousands of calving wildebeest and the splendours of the Serengeti plains. 'I found it incredible that a man who has spent thirty years in the bush still had such passion for wildlife despite all his problems.' says Piers. 'Tristan was under enormous pressure, but he just went on and on about how magical the Serengeti had been.'

It was dark by the time Tristan got back to Deloraine that evening and too late to drive up to Sosian. Cindy remembers her husband being much distracted and incensed by the loss of Richard's house, but he also described wildebeest calving on the Serengeti plains, likening it to a spectacle from the Pliocene era. Before leaving the following morning, Tristan sent his pilot, Alex Rechsteiner, an email thanking him for the flight to Nairobi and mourning the destruction of Richard's house. 'A third and perhaps the nicest house was burnt while I was waiting at Kili, so in some respects I am too late,' he lamented, 'although only a twenty per cent shareholder in our scheme, I did put the deal together, so dreams are literally up in smoke as I write.'

Tristan's next email was to commiserate with his friend. 'Dear Richard, I am speechless and have never been more so,' he admitted. 'For some reason your loss is more of a stab than the other houses. I sent an app yesterday to say we must do something to protect it, but I got the news too late as I was prepared to sleep on your veranda. You had made that house wonderful. It makes me weep to think of it. I am going up to Sosian now and will report soonest. Please do not bother to reply and I am sure we shall talk soon. Very best and big hug, Tristan.'

As Tristan left with a cold box of supplies prepared by his wife on the back seat, Cindy bade him farewell with a caution. 'You don't need be a hero,' she said.

Tristan followed the road he had driven countless times before on his way to Sosian, and having passed the sign to Ol Maisor, pulled his Land

Rover off the road to review the smouldering ruins of Richard's house through binoculars. He arrived at Sosian without incident, but ten minutes later, a security vehicle came under fire crossing the bridge over the Ewaso Nyiro River, less than five hundred yards from Sean's house.

Earlier in the day, a police helicopter was targeted while flying over the northern section of Sosian Ranch, and the police commander's convoy and another farm vehicle had also been attacked. Tristan learnt that police had been embroiled in a morning ambush, five miles from the lodge, and that several cattle were killed when they were used as living shields from police bullets.

The destruction of the lodge, houses and other buildings clustered together at Sosian was the invaders' ultimate goal; however, the lodge occupies an elevated position and is surrounded by solid dry-stone walls providing solid fortification. But the greatest deterrents were two armoured cars parked outside Sean's office and roof-mounted with 7.62-millimetre general purpose machine guns. Despite their presence, the day-long battle had neared the bridge at times, and was still raging when Tristan, Jonti and Sean sat down on the veranda of Rosy and Simon's house to talk above a backdrop of intermittent gunfire.

Tristan quarrelled with Sean, who was adamant that he should not go anywhere near Richard's ransacked home, and refused to sanction the use of a company car. Tristan retaliated by saying that he would walk up there the next day, and laughed off Sean's warning that he would almost certainly be shot if he attempted to do so. Tristan's reaction to the general manager's well-intentioned advice was a bridge too far for Sean, who had borne the brunt of the invaders' aggression for the last month and was in no mood for another argument. He stood up, and walked back across sunburnt lawns to his own house.

Fittingly, one of the last emails Tristan ever sent was to the man who gave him his first job in Africa and set him firmly on the path to success as a businessman, safari guide and conservationist. Before dinner, he wrote to thank Tony Church for his efforts to galvanise KWS into action, tapping out the words as shots continued to ring out from the surrounding bush.

'Now we are under siege with up to 100 police here,' he explained. 'We have pleaded for them to stop the operation and go home as they are useless, but then we need a fairly large presence to stop the enemy attacking and torching the lodge. Archie is up the way on Gilfrid's and under siege too, so it has sadly escalated.'

He continued, 'I am very surprised at Richard Leakey's reaction to your letter. The politics, cattle, land degradation in the north and more than just apathy by Government are mind boggling. What has happened at Mugie, Kifuku, Suyian and now us is on a Zimbabwean scale of land grabbing and will have serious repercussions down the line. The Northern Rangelands are gone forever and Laikipia would last five minutes if these guys took over the ranches.'

When Tristan telephoned Cindy later the same evening, he was more cheerful than she had expected, although Jonti compared his last evening with Tristan to being holed up in a patrol base in Northern Ireland, but without the level of protection and support the former soldiers could have expected from the British Army.

The two close friends spent much of the evening discussing the reasons for Sosian's current plight, but Tristan also told Jonti how happy he was to have Cindy back home at Deloraine, and how proud he was of both Archie and Imo. But whatever the chat between them, by the time Tristan went to bed his mind was made up. He would ride up to Richard Constant's house the next day, and nobody was going to stop him.

Tristan and Sean left Sosian on the morning of Sunday 5th March in a convoy of two cars; Sean was taking security personnel loaned by Ol Pejeta back to Rumuruti to collect their own vehicle after a two-day stay, and Tristan was giving Jonti a lift back to Ol Maisor for his plane. Before leaving, at 8.46 a.m. Tristan sent his wife a text. 'Quiet night but all rather stressful.' By the time Cindy replied, Tristan was drinking coffee with Jonti and Martin Evans on the veranda at Ol Maisor, during which there was no mention of a visit to Richard's house, although Tristan had told Sean he was planning to visit Archie at Suyian.

Tristan stayed only long enough to be polite, thanked the Evans's for their hospitality, and drove quickly back to Sosian, where he asked for a favourite grey stallion to be tacked up and made ready to ride. The horse was called Loita, named after the range of hills that were the starting point for so many Offbeat riding safaris in the early days. Barend tried to dissuade

Tristan, but found him in no mood for compromise, only adamant that he was to blame for introducing investors to Sosian in the first place.

'Don't worry,' Tristan said, fixing him with a glare from his steel blue eyes, 'no one is going to shoot an unarmed mzungu[44] riding a horse, but if they want to, that's just the way it is. I'll be back in a couple of hours.' The time was 11.00 a.m.

Down at the stables, the head syce, John Ekiru, led Loita out to the mounting block and begged Tristan not to ride anywhere near Richard's house, where the thick scrub concealed dozens of trigger-happy intruders. David Macharia hurried down from the lodge with a radio in his outstretched hand, but Tristan declined the offer, explaining that carrying one could be misconstrued as liaising with the police. 'We tried our best to stop him from going,' remembers John, 'but he would not listen to us.'

Ever courteous, Tristan thanked both men for their concern, swung his leg over the saddle and turned Loita's head for the hills. Loita was John's best lead horse, an animal that could be relied upon to go unhesitatingly first past elephant, lion, and buffalo, but on this Sunday morning he was reluctant to leave the yard. Tristan had to gather up the reins and give him a good dig in the ribs before the stallion stepped out onto the driveway and settled to his task.

John watched through binoculars as Loita pricked up his ears on his way down to the bridge spanning a brown dribble of water. He saw them cross the main road where two dirt tracks collide in the desert, break into a trot on the far side, and then canter uphill until they were swallowed up from sight by the bush.

The soil is thin at the top of the hill, and has been worn away in places to reveal hard, grey slabs of rock that clink beneath the hooves of a horse and soak up the heat of a pitiless sun. Tristan slowed to a walk here and let Loita pick his way carefully across the rock field, past fig trees spouting from colossal boulders, to higher ground, where ivory spikes bristle like porcupine quills from the branches of wait-a-bit thorns. A group of tall, slim men dressed in kikoys and cradling assault rifles beneath their arms scarcely gave him a second glance as they passed away to one side

---

44 A white person.

chattering amongst themselves. They were an advance party preparing the way for thousands of thirsty cattle that had spent the night bomaed on the cold, high plains to come down and drink from the river.

As Tristan rode east to the boundary with Suyian Ranch, the sun felt hot on his face; if he had turned to look back he would have seen the fried-egg profile of The Aberdare Range simmering above parched plains, and away to his right, the faint outline of Mount Kenya, and the hazy rim of the Great Rift Valley baking in the midday sun.

When Sean heard that Tristan had left for Richard's house on horseback, the manager was 'ninety-nine-per-cent convinced' that Tristan would be shot, but he had one last card to play. He called Archie, who was out on the ranch at Suyian, and asked him to drive up to the track his father must ride along to reach Richard's house, and intercept him before it was too late. Archie met Tristan where the track meets the ragged stone wall marking the boundary between the two ranches, but was unable to dissuade him from his mission.

Instead they made a plan to meet at an open gateway half a mile further along the wall, which Archie hoped would give him time to question some of the trespassers wandering about Suyian, and establish if it was safe for his father to continue. Archie found no one to help, but when he arrived at the rendezvous, there was no sign of his father either. The minutes passed interminably slowly as Archie waited beside the boundary wall, and shots rang out from somewhere beyond the bulge of high ground that hid Richard's house from his view.

Archie realised his father must have cut across country for the last half mile of his ride and walked forward to the crest of the ridge. From this vantage point he looked out across a dry valley and depleted dam to the silhouette of a burnt-out wreck. There was no sign of life in the scarred and silent vista, just the disfigured remains of stranded walls and a tall stone chimney piercing the bright blue sky. Before Archie had time to survey the ruins through his binoculars, the silence was shattered by gunfire, and bullets slammed into the scrub beside him. He sprinted back over the ridge to his waiting vehicle, and drove to Suyian with a pounding heart and the accelerator pressed hard to the floor.

By then messages were starting to filter through to Sean via the bush telegraph of mobile telephones that Tristan had been shot, but it was far too dangerous for any white man to approach Richard's house. Archie took to the skies with Gilfrid, but it was not safe to fly at low altitude, and from fifteen-hundred-feet up all that could be seen was a saddleless Loita standing disconsolate and injured beside the dam.

Neighbours in a second light aircraft and a helicopter also flew in to help, but after the aerial search was abandoned, a Laikipiak Maasai from Sosian's security team bravely volunteered to go and look for Tristan on foot. Peter Lechoromongi parked his motorbike a mile from the house and walked in dressed in mufti. He found Tristan's body lying on the grass outside the house; there was a carpet and a bathmat where he fell, and three bullet holes in his body.

Epilogue

IT WAS not possible to collect Tristan's body by police helicopter until the following day, after which he was flown down to Nairobi for formal identification. His horse, Loita, was killed and eaten by Pokot invaders on the night of his murder, and never seen again. Four days later, a large crowd of local people including Deloraine employees, teachers and students from the Leldet Primary School, gathered behind Tristan's coffin on the front lawn to pay their last respects at a special community service.

Cindy addressed her guests eloquently, thanking them for attending and offering support. She spoke of her family's comfort that Tristan died defending a cause he believed in, and her husband's honourable commitment to Kenya and the preservation of its habitat and wildlife. She also paid tribute to the family home of the last twenty-four years, thanking the board of the Rift Valley Institute of Science and Technology for making it all possible, and reminding mourners of how hard Tristan worked to preserve and protect the forest and surrounding land. Most of all, Cindy hoped that her husband had not died in vain, and pledged to continue his good work.

After the service, a funeral pyre was lit behind the house. There was a hard, hot wind billowing up from the plains below, which fanned the fire into a raging inferno and quickly consumed Tristan's body.

More than seven hundred mourners gathered on the lawns at Deloraine to celebrate Tristan's life the following day, including friends and family from the UK and beyond. They arrived in cars, station wagons, taxis, Jeeps, trucks, Land Rovers and by air. Those who had travelled the furthest pulled into the open gateway of a large grass field at the bottom of the garden to read a chart indicating the location of their tent for the night, just as a guest might scrutinise a seating plan before entering a marquee at a party. They found each tent carefully numbered with camp beds, washing facilities, and deck chairs beneath the awning, laid out as if for a safari in the African bush.

The drought that had gripped Kenya for months was not yet done, and the congregation sitting on hay bales set out in a quiet corner of the garden looked out across scorched lawns to a line of sleek, sunlit polo ponies, watching proceedings with ears cocked towards the crowd. Between hymns, they listened to readings where voices seemed at times to be drowned by the vastness of Africa; they heard poignant poetry recitals from Cindy and Imo, and the familiar, stirring tale of 'The Man from Snowy River', only this time the words were spoken by Archie, not his father.

The Barclays paid moving tribute to their friend; Jonti recalled the transformation of Sosian from a barren waste into a land of plenty, and the treasured moments of humour, pride and nostalgia that surfaced during his last night with Tristan at a ranch under siege. He struck a chord when complaining that Tristan really should have given his family and friends at least another ten years, but that life as a grumpy old man would not have suited him at all.

When the hunting horn rang out above the silent congregation, every pony lifted its head in an expression of alert anticipation, but the vibrant notes marked the end of formal proceedings, not the start of a hunt with the ghosts of Ginger Bell's pack. After the service, many of Tristan's relatives and friends relived their own special memories from the front steps of Deloraine house, before celebrating his life late into the night.

By lunchtime the next day, a small group had left in light aircraft and four-wheel-drive vehicles on a mission to honour a request Tristan had made many times during his life. They found the Masai Mara shimmering with the vivid green blush that follows rain, and met giraffe, elephant and lion on the drive to the campsite at Olare Lamun. A poem was read out before dinner describing love for a sunburnt country, the extremes of drought, floods, beauty and terror, and the transformation wrought by life-sustaining rain. The party left camp early the next morning for Oloiburmut, the steep, thorny hillside where countless safari clients had admired panoramic views from the rocky summit. Cindy carried a small wooden box containing Tristan's remains on the twenty-minute hike, along game tracks twisting through long grass and clutching thorns, to the open clearing at the top of the hill.

After his ashes had been cast off the summit and drifted down onto the plains below, bones were placed carefully amongst giant grey rocks and the curved, elephantine roots of a bustling fig tree. Friends and family lingered in silent contemplation for an hour or more, before walking from the hill and leaving Tristan alone with the wildlife beneath a hot blue sky.

There were no polo ponies or wild game at Tristan's memorial service four months later, but the sun was still shining brightly to welcome hundreds of guests to the parish church at Greens Norton on a sweltering hot English afternoon. Morven and Rufus both spoke of their brother's remarkable life, the latter commenting on the boundless generosity and unflinching loyalty that won him so many friends.

'It was amazing how many people called Tristan their best friend,' Rufus mused, 'and how many safari goers arrived as punters but left as good mates.' There were more tributes, readings and recitals, and rousing trumpeters from the Blues and Royals, before the wake got underway beside the lake on Sorrel and James Shepherd-Cross's Northamptonshire farm.

Rufus had also spoken of his brother's love for Africa and her wildlife, and Tristan's sadness 'at the way things were going' on the continent he so adored. Laikipia County will never be quite the same after the 2017 invasions, which left conservationists, farmers and inhabitants irrevocably bruised by the scale and savagery of the invasions. Ostensibly, peace had returned to the region by the time of Tristan's memorial, for the Kenya Defence Force had moved in soon after his death to restore law and order.

The Laikipia North MP, Mathew Lempurkel, had been arrested within days of Tristan's murder, but incitement charges were dropped due to a lack of evidence. No one knows if Tristan's killers will ever be brought to justice, but Lempurkel was trounced at the general elections in August 2017 by Sarah Korere, the rival he had allegedly beaten, insulted and intimidated nine months earlier.

The severe drought that had provided a smokescreen for land invasions broke in May 2017, and Laikipia was green once more. Wildlife gradually started to reappear at Sosian after the invaders and their cattle had departed, repopulating a recently hostile land in the manner that has been the gift of African wildlife since the beginning of time. Sosian Lodge reopened for business on a self-catering basis at the end of 2017, and by

June the following year, new lodge managers were ready to welcome visitors and continue high standards nurtured by the Nels, Careys and more recently, Simon Kenyon and Rosy Constant.

None of the three Sosian shareholders whose houses were razed to the ground has yet started to rebuild. Perhaps some of them never will, although Richard Constant is determined to resurrect his former home and make it stronger than before. There are no regrets, not even from Christl, whose close friend and Archie's employer, Gilfrid Powys, was tragically killed on his Suyian Ranch by an elephant just after Christmas 2017. 'I spent the most wonderful seventeen years at Sosian,' she says. 'I have no regrets at all, but it's finished now for me.'

As a consequence of these invasions, income from tourism income had completely dried up, obliging the shareholders and Sean Outram to reappraise the way Sosian will be run in future. They still aspire to encourage and protect wildlife on the ranch, but they have had to look at alternative revenue streams.

One option is to fence off some two thousand five hundred acres of land for the cultivation of crops such as hay, wheat and sorghum. Another is to increase stocking densities across the ranch, which naturally reduces an excess of dry-season grazing that trespassers found hard to resist. The owners of many other Laikipian properties feel the same way; according to Sean Outram, at least twenty thousand acres will fall to the plough in western Laikipia as a direct consequence of the 2016 and 2017 land invasions.

It is hard to know what Tristan would have made of these sweeping changes – he had been vehemently opposed to cropping anywhere on Sosian when alive, but the pragmatist within would surely have accepted the wisdom of sacrificing ten per cent of her land mass, in order to preserve the remaining ninety per cent. Unlike pasture, cultivated land is protected from trespassers by much stronger laws, and strategic crop production also helps feed the nation, while continuing to provide habitat and space for wildlife.

Sean is also building up cattle densities on Sosian to a rate of one cow per ten acres and offering share-grazing options to local communities. This will mean a little less grass for wildlife, but a much-reduced risk of the slaughter that followed armed invasions in 2017. Despite all the recent troubles, Sosian might yet have made the perfect retirement home that Tristan always dreamed of.

Under Cindy and Imo's organisation, Offbeat riding safaris are as popular and well-supported as ever, and although it is inconceivable that any one person could replace their founder's unique charisma, young guides such as Simon Kenyon, Joss Craig and Megan Hodgson have been widely praised. In March 2018, family and friends rode across a stormy but spectacular Mara landscape on a week-long memorial ride guided by Archie, taking a rare break from his duties at Suyian. The group included Cindy and Imo, Freddie Menzies, Tristan's friend since Folkington days, and Garth Thompson, who Tristan rated as one of the top guides in all Africa.

Eight weeks later, nine hundred people attended a glittering ball in London organised by Imo to launch the Tristan Voorspuy Conservation Trust, which will support charities preserving natural biodiversity in partnership with local communities, through increased awareness, family planning, and education. These causes were close to Tristan's heart; after his death, Cindy found an unfinished letter to the KWS, which lays the blame for Kenya's catastrophic loss of wildlife and habitat firmly at the door of population increase and poverty.

'I have taken the decision to appeal directly to you, as I feel that wildlife in Kenya is at crisis level and only an immediate radical change in its management will save it long-term in Kenya. We do not have much time,' he warned. 'Kenya wildlife has changed beyond all recognition in the last 20 years and human population increase with the poverty cycle still well in place is the chief cause.'

Back at Deloraine, life continues apace. Cindy has remained true to the pledges she gave to the local community, and is determined to continue Tristan's good work in every sphere of operation. The Voorspuys' family life still revolves around the rose-tinted stone house with mangalore tiles, open-air verandas and colourful gardens on the western edge of the Great Rift Valley. In the forest behind Deloraine, the wildlife goes quietly and unobtrusively about its business, surviving in a forest Tristan strove to protect and preserve from destruction.

The rhino and bongo will never return, but in an extraordinary twist of fate, Tristan's last and ultimately fatal journey to Sosian the day before he died was delayed by the appearance of three young bull elephants at Deloraine. The gentle giants had been spotted early that morning on Gogar, heading towards the refuge of Londiani Mountain. Cindy set off on horseback to investigate, while Tristan took to his Land Rover to search for an animal no one could remember seeing in the area for decades.

Halfway up the mountain, where the air is so pure that the sea-green lichen flutters from the branches and the woodland smells earthy, dank and mysterious, the three bachelor elephants shifted quietly on soft feet and unfurled long, grey trunks through the trees. In places, sunlight pierced the canopy to light up fragments of gleaming ivory, as white tusks swayed unhurriedly back and forth to the rhythm of the elephants' repast. They heard the muted growl of Tristan's Land Rover far beneath them, and when Cindy rode up into the forest, the distant rattle of drumming hoof beats on a forest path, but although Cindy found giant footprints below the dam, the Voorspuys never caught up with their visitors.

The three males were refugees from the ravaged lands of Laikipia, taking days to unravel an ancestral trail to Londiani that had not been used since their forebears abandoned the route seventy years earlier. The visitors may have fled the Marmanet region of western Laikipia, but are likely to have roamed with their parents across Sosian's wild landscape and drunk from the brown waters of Ewaso Nyiro River during Tristan's tenure of the ranch.

Perhaps he had already seen them in happier times, on horseback, from a vehicle or on foot. Up until the 1950s, the ninety-mile journey would have been relatively straightforward for a pachyderm, but a steady intensification of farming, roads, railways and urbanisation were thought to have extinguished formerly well-remembered elephant trails all over the Rift Valley. The elusive visitors sought refuge on the wooded slopes of Londiani for months after Tristan's death, only venturing downhill under the cover of darkness to drink, knock down fences, and raid smallholders' maize fields.

Elephants returned to Deloraine at the time of Tristan's memorial service in England, then disappeared for several weeks, moving higher up the mountain towards the bamboo-covered crater at the summit, where their wanderings were shrouded in secrecy. They came back down the mountain at the end of August, and were seen for the first time by Imo as she led a group of riders out from under the trees to enjoy the view across the Rift Valley from the Top of the World.

As her horse stepped into a glade dotted with lucky bean trees, whose tiny fruits had decorated the service sheets at her father's funeral, Imo heard the crash of shaking bushes and breaking timber ahead. At first, she thought the noise was made by cattle, but quickly realised the tall grey backs retreating into the forest belonged to her father's favourite animal. Although they continued to leave behind signs of their nocturnal travels – piles of steaming dung, broken fences and footprints around water troughs – no one saw the elephants again. After a while their visits became less frequent, until finally they did not come back to Deloraine at all.

Principal Characters

Astley Birtwistle, Pip: A close friend of Tristan's ever since joining him at Sandhurst in 1975.

Barclay, Jonti: Youngest son of Petre Barclay; one of the first Sosian shareholders, whose family are close friends of the Voorspuys.

Barclay, Petre: Owns Madrugada close to Deloraine, and assisted the Voorspuys' move to Deloraine.

Bateman, Peter: Was on the same SAS course as Tristan in 1981 and joined him for the Sussex to Cape Town motorbike ride in 1982. Now runs a boatyard in Kilifi.

Bell, Ginger: Former butcher and master of Ginger Bell's Hunt, he left the hounds to Tristan in his will. Deceased.

Bower, Tom: Part-owned a ranch in Laikipia called Mutara, where Morven Voorspuy took Tristan on his first visit to Kenya in 1974. Deceased.

Camm, Hector: Younger son of Johnny and Lucy Camm. Tristan's godson.

Camm, Johnny: Computer programmer and polo-playing friend of Tristan's who was killed in a gyrocopter accident in 2000.

Camm, Lucy (née Vigne): Wife of Johnny who is based in Karen, Nairobi and works in wildlife research. A close friend of Tristan's ever since their first meeting in the 1980s.

Camm, Rufus: Eldest son of Johnny and Lucy above.

Carey, Steve and Annabelle: Arrived at Sosian in 2007 to run the lodge, and stayed for five years. They now run their own safari camp in Laikipia.

Church, Tony: Pioneering Kenyan riding safari operator, who developed the concept of riding across wild Africa on horseback supported by a full crew of camp staff. Gave Tristan his first job in Africa in 1983.

Constant, Richard: Riding safari client from England, who bought a share in Sosian, built a house on the property, and became good friends with Tristan.

Constant, Rosy: Daughter of Richard. Worked at Sosian after leaving school and returned to run the lodge there with Simon Kenyon in 2012.

Deal, Anthony: Successful businessman from England; last investor to come on board at Sosian.

Evans, Martin: Owns Ol Maisor Ranch in Laikipia, and after putting down a deposit on Sosian in 1999, persuaded Tristan to form a consortium and complete the purchase.

Fox, Bayard and Mel: Wyoming-based tour operators, who met Tristan when he guided his first safari for Tony Church in 1983 and later supported Offbeat Safaris after Tristan's split from Safaris Unlimited.

Grant, Hamish: Old Etonian farming neighbour of the Voorspuys at Gogar. Witnessed Rory Hensman's elephant demonstration with Tristan at Braeside in 2000.

Hensman, Rory: Farmer and elephant trainer who became a lifelong friend of Tristan's after inviting him and other friends to stay at Braeside, his farm near Chinhoyi in Zimbabwe, during Tristan's 1982 bike ride. Deceased.

Hensman, Sean: Son of Rory; also worked for Offbeat Safaris as a back-up rider.

Keene, Julieta: Argentine, who came out to Kenya to work for the Voorspuys as a young woman in 2000 and stayed for two years.

Kenyon, Jackie and Mandy: Owners of Mogwooni Ranch in Laikipia and close friends of the Voorspuys. Jackie also worked on the *Out of Africa* film set with Tristan in 1985.

Kenyon, Simon: Son of Jackie and Mandy. Worked for Offbeat Safaris on an ad-hoc basis and ran Sosian Lodge with Rosy Constant from 2012–2017.

Knight Bruce, Robin: A friend of Tristan's from childhood and army days.

Knocker, Will: Employed by Tristan to reach a management agreement with the Maasai owners of Ol Kinyei Group Ranch in 1995.

Laurence, Mark: Former professional jockey in Kenya and UK. Started work as a full-time riding safari guide for Offbeat Safaris in September 1994 and stayed for twelve years.

Lee, Martyn: Lifelong friend of Tristan's and his best man.

Macharia, David: Assistant manager at Sosian since the very beginning.

Macintosh, Brian and Angela: Cindy's parents. Brian managed Lewa Downs in Laikipia before returning to manage farms in the UK.

Macoun, Brian: A close friend of the Voorspuys who worked for Anglo American and Lonrho. His mother was brought up at Fintry next to Deloraine and Brian was also Pam Scott's godson.

McConnell, Charlie and Mouse: Joint owners of Robin Hurt Safaris who first met Tristan soon after his arrival in Kenya. Charlie and Mouse both worked on the *Out of Africa* film set with him in 1985.

McLellan, Philip (aka Flip Flop) and Katie: Polo playing, drag hunting, flying and safari friends of the Voorspuys who met when their children were born in Nairobi hospital in 1992. Tristan was in Philip's plane when it nearly crashed over the Ruaha National Park in 1985.

Menzies, Freddie: Lifelong friend of Tristan's since childhood.

Nel, Hannes and Lorian: Couple who came to run Sosian Ranch and Lodge soon after purchase in 2000 and helped transform the property.

Orme-Smith, Chris and Teresa: Safari organisers who were original shareholders at Sosian. Chris now deceased.

Outram, Sean: Arrived at Sosian aged twenty-six in 2006 with Charlotte Roger-Smith to run the ranch and establish a herd of pedigree boran cattle. Married Charlotte in 2010 and in 2012 was promoted to the positon of general manager. Bore the brunt of the 2017 land invasions and remains the general manager at Sosian.

Potgieter, Willy and Nicky: Became good friends of the Voorspuys after they moved to Rongai close to Deloraine in 1994 to start an ornamental flower seed business. Willy witnessed Tristan's near fatal accident in a gyrocopter at Gogar in 1999.

Powys, Gilfrid: Owner of Suyian Ranch. A member of the pioneering early white settler family that arrived in Laikipia in 1914, he became Tristan's neighbour after the purchase of Sosian in 1999 and later Archie Voorspuy's employer. Gilfrid was killed by an elephant at Suyian in December 2017.

Purcell, Roland: Close friend of Tristan's from early days in Africa and founder of Greystoke Camp in Mahale Mountains National Park on the shores of Lake Tanganyika. Roland helped Tristan fly his new plane back to Kenya from England on an epic journey in 1994.

Roger-Smith, Charlotte: Arrived at Sosian in 2006 with Sean Outram to run the lodge and the following year opened the Offbeat Safaris office in Nanyuki. Married Sean in 2010.

Ryrie, Elizabeth (now Glaysher): Tristan's girlfriend for six years from 1979, and a good friend ever since. Brought up at Rosslyn in Nairobi, where her mother continued to live for many years.

Ryrie, Sonia: Mother of Elizabeth who helped Tristan learn Swahili soon after his arrival in Kenya and was a generous and hospitable hostess to him on many occasions.

Scott, Pamela (Pam): The former owner of Deloraine who made a great success of running the farming enterprise there before selling in 1979. Pam continued to live as a tenant at Deloraine until her death in 1992, after which the Voorspuys moved in.

Shepherd-Cross, Sorrel (second marriage, formerly Woods): Tristan's elder sister. Mother of Tam, Toby and Dom Woods.

Theobald, Bimb: Entrepreneur who arrived in Kenya at the same time as Tristan and went on to develop several successful businesses. They met and lived together in The Bunker in Nairobi when Tristan was working for Tony Church, and then other houses in Lavington and Karen before both were married.

Thompson, Garth: Good friend of Tristan's and an acclaimed safari guide and brilliant photographer.

Vigne, Lucy: Married Johnny Camm, see Lucy Camm.

von Plessen, Christl: Mother of Jakob and Sosian shareholder who designed and furnished the lodge at Sosian.

von Plessen, Jakob: Argentine who started work for Offbeat Safaris in 1999 when eighteen years old and stayed for several years. Now runs his own riding holidays in Patagonia.

Voorspuy, Archie: Tristan and Cindy's son, born 1992.

Voorspuy, Lucinda (Cindy; née Macintosh): Tristan's wife, whom he married in 1989.

Voorspuy, Hendrik (Henk): Tristan's father. Flew with Bomber Command during the Second World War and later worked as an airline pilot for the Dutch airline, KLM. Deceased.

Voorspuy, Imogen, (Imo): Tristan and Cindy's daughter, born 1994.

Voorspuy, Morven: Tristan's elder brother. Former farmer and airline pilot. Took Tristan on his first visit to Kenya in 1974. Father of Camilla, Roxy, Ferdie and Hedley.

Voorspuy, Pearl (née Glessing): Tristan's mother and wife of Henk. Deceased.

Voorspuy, Rufus: Tristan's brother and the eldest sibling. Former racehorse trainer, now lives in Scotland. Father of Thady and Holly.

Watson, Rupert: Lawyer friend of Tristan's, who helped register and set up Offbeat Safaris in 1999.

Winkworth, Piers: Came out to Kenya to work for Offbeat in 2002, and in 2005 invested in Offbeat Safaris by building Offbeat Mara and Meru camps.

Acknowledgements

THIS BOOK would never have got off the ground without the involvement and support of so many different people. Top of the list are the Voorspuy family, who have been unfailingly helpful, patient and co-operative. I would especially like to thank Cindy Voorspuy, who has encouraged this project from the start, provided Tristan's fascinating diaries, organised an enlightening research trip to Kenya, and responded quickly and accurately to my unrelenting barrage of questions.

They say that every cloud has a silver lining, and one of the great pleasures of writing this book has been getting to know Tristan's brothers, sister, nephew and nieces, all of whom have been unswervingly helpful. Sorrel and James Shepherd-Cross have offered up their charming house in central England as a base for meetings and research on several occasions, and I would also like to thank Sorrel, Rufus, Morven and Cindy's own parents for allowing me to read and quote from some very intimate letters.

I owe a debt of gratitude to everyone who has responded to my questions, whether in person, by email, WhatsApp or telephone. There are way too many to acknowledge individually, but in Africa I would particularly like to thank Tony Church, Lucy Camm, Jonti Barclay, Mark Laurence, Sean Outram and Rupert Watson, all of whom were closely wrapped up in Tristan's Kenyan life, as well as Peter Bateman for his fascinating account of the 1984 bike ride, and Sean Hensman for his guidance on the elephant chapter.

Thanks also to those kind families and individuals who extended generous hospitality during my recent visit to their country: Lucy Camm in Karen, Elizabeth Glaysher and Sonia Ryrie at Rosslyn, Hamish Grant at Gogar, Martin Evans at Ol Maisor, Jackie and Mandy Kenyon at Mogwooni, Archie Voorspuy and Izzy Parsons at Suyian, Brian Macoun in Nairobi and, of course, Cindy and Imo at Deloraine and all the wonderful staff who help keep that magnificent show on the road.

It is hard to establish exactly where some of Tristan's friends live, especially Roland Purcell, who seemed to be in a different part of the world whenever we spoke, but I am grateful for his invaluable assistance with chapter nine. Also in the UK or thereabouts are Elizabeth Glaysher, Freddie Menzies, Martin Horsford, Martyn Lee, Piers Winkworth, Pip Astley Birtwistle, Richard Constant, Robin Knight Bruce and Xan Smiley, who has an almost encyclopaedic knowledge of Deloraine house. And I must not forget the Argentines, Julieta Keene and Jakob von Plessen, who were an integral part of the Offbeat team, and a great help to me in writing this book.

Others have contributed by providing detailed accounts of incidents that took place on safari and elsewhere, often long ago. These include the late Gilfrid Powys, Mel and Bayard Fox, Charlie and Mouse McConnell, Philip McLellan, Xandi Maculen, Bill Vanderbilt, Willy Potgieter, Anne Buckley, Natalie McComb, Kitty Graham and Georgi Wickham, who witnessed the extraordinary Maasai lion hunt in 1997. If I have any regrets, they are not being able to include so many other excellent stories that have found their way to my desk. To those that sent them, a heartfelt thanks, and apologies that they have not made it into print. Thank you also to those kind individuals who have provided photographs to be used in this book, including the Voorspuy family, all of Tristan's siblings, Elizabeth Glaysher, Garth Thompson, Guy Hanmer, Lindie Hensman, Lucy Camm, Martyn Lee, Peter Bateman, Pip Astley Birtwistle and Tony Church and anyone else whose generosity has been overlooked.

This is my second book for Quiller Publishing, and I am so grateful for Andrew and Gilly Johnston's continued support and all the superb team, including Arabella Ainslie, Becky Bowyer, Harry Johnston and Matthew Collis. This has been my first experience of working with an editor, and I would like to thank Clare Grist Taylor for her steadfast support, encouragement and advice. I have suggested on more than one occasion that she must have easier writers to work with than myself, but she has always shrugged off any frustrations and we can look back on an absorbing and rewarding journey over these last nine months.

Finally, but by no means the least, I pay tribute to my former wife, Rachel, who was a constant source of advice, inspiration and guidance during the writing of this book, and more than anyone else, had to bear the brunt of a sometimes introspective and self-centred outlook that seems to be the writer's lot.

Adrian Dangar

The Tristan Voorspuy
Conservation Trust

THE TRISTAN Voorspuy Conservation Trust (TVCT) has been set up by his family to cherish the memory of Tristan and to continue and enhance his philanthropic legacy of protecting Kenya's wildlife – both flora and fauna – for the future.

The fast-growing, and in many cases poverty-stricken population of rural Kenya was always at the forefront of Tristan's mind, primarily due to the enormous and increasing pressure that this has put on the land and wildlife. Tristan saw the need to help people, often living in marginal areas, to save their biodiversity through education and support.

The Trust promotes this message by funding recognised charities that share its mission to enhance the harmonious coexistence of animals and humans on the land they both inhabit. It believes that education and family planning go hand in hand towards finding the key to sustainability. Allowing women to choose how many children they have, and the space between each child, gives both mother and children a brighter future. We believe that wildlife has the best chance of survival when those communities, wildlife custodians for millennia, can enjoy its value and benefits.

To avoid overheads and operational costs, the Trust is fund-donating, supporting chosen charity projects, often with limited means, to be as effective as possible. Its first charity partner is CHASE Africa, which operates mobile clinics offering free primary healthcare and family planning, and supports educational facilities and the planting of trees. Their pragmatic approach is a fitting tribute to Tristan's vision of the co-development of conservation and local communities.